*The*

*Life as a student nurse in the 1960s*

# The Calling

## Life as a student nurse in the 1960s

Molly Brearley RGN, RM, RHV

A CIP catalogue record for this book is available from the British Library.

ISBN 978-0-9954759-0-8

Book layout and cover design by Clare Brayshaw

Prepared and printed by:

York Publishing Services Ltd
64 Hallfield Road
Layerthorpe
York YO31 7ZQ

Tel: 01904 431213

Website: www. yps-publishing. co. uk

*Author Molly Brearley (front left)*

*Molly as a newly qualified nurse (on the left)*

# Chapter 1

The journey seemed endless, as I sat watching the hypnotic movement of the windscreen wipers from the back seat of Dad's car. Would we ever arrive at our destination? Dad's Austin A35 didn't go very fast. It was a dark, wet, miserable day in January 1966. I was feeling extremely anxious. Mum was sitting in the passenger seat, occasionally making pleasant conversation in an attempt to relax me. I was leaving the security of the small terrace house in Cullingworth where I had been brought up and travelling to Huddersfield to start my general nurse training. As I was still only seventeen years old, I would have to work as a cadet nurse for several months, eighteen being the minimum age to start proper training.

How had I come to make this journey? I had never considered becoming a nurse, and knew very little about it apart from watching *Dr Kildare* on the television, where the nurses did look rather glamorous in their uniforms. I hated senior school, was disinterested in most subjects, deciding to leave at sixteen with no idea what I wanted to do. There were few job opportunities open to females in the 1960s.

The most common jobs for women were secretarial work, shop assistant, hairdressing, teaching or nursing. I had discussed my future with the youth employment officer who suggested a college in Leeds where I could do a pre-nursing course. It was a two year course where I would continue my general education plus subjects required for nursing. I would also have an insight into practical nursing, having a hospital placement for a day each week in the first year, with two days a week in the second year. I reluctantly agreed; it would at least allow me to leave school.

The traditional control that doctors and matrons held over nurses' education was changing. By 1962 the regulator, the General Nursing Council had re-introduced a minimum standard of entry for nurse training, something that had been suspended when the second world war began. The minimum standard of entry was five GCE O-levels or passing the hospital entrance examination.

Mum was pleased when I was accepted on the course and relished telling people that her daughter was going to train to be a nurse. She would often comment that nursing was "a calling" and "not just a job". I never fully understood what she meant as I definitely never felt "called".

I had thoroughly enjoyed my time at college, made lots of friends and life had become more interesting. It felt as if a light had been switched on in my brain, and I had become eager to learn. The tutors had been encouraging and helpful. I had been introduced to new subjects like anatomy and physiology, and I had begun to get good grades in my examinations.

I had enjoyed my hospital placements which had enabled me to spend time with patients and practise some basic nursing skills. The two years had flown by and lots of tears had been shed on our last day. Most of my college friends were starting their training at Leeds General Infirmary but hopefully we would keep in touch.

I had decided to go to Huddersfield as a new hospital

was being built, due for completion soon after I began my training. I was not familiar with the area, only having visited once before for my interview at the Old Infirmary, which had been built in 1830 by Joseph Kay and opened in 1831 at a cost of £7,500.

Huddersfield seemed an interesting place, a large market town in the Metropolitan Borough of Kirklees in West Yorkshire. It is a town of Victorian architecture, known for its role in the Industrial Revolution, and for being the birthplace of the British Prime Minister Harold Wilson. It has a large variety of shops, pubs, restaurants and discotheques, which were not enclosed within the town's ring road as they are today. Castle Hill dominates the local landscape: the summit is by far the most conspicuous landmark of Huddersfield. Victoria Tower, perched on the hill, was completed in 1899 to celebrate the sixtieth anniversary of Queen Victoria's reign.

I felt excited that I would be living there for the next three years: it would be a complete life change for me. Fortunately I would only be sixteen miles from home, far enough to be independent, and near enough if I was feeling homesick.

Dad was humming a tune from the past while concentrating on his driving. Mum was quietly reading.

The hospital loomed in the distance; we were almost there.

# Chapter 2

Dad parked the car in the hospital car park and got my luggage from the boot. The three of us went in through the imposing front door and were directed to Matron's office. Walking down the long dark corridor, my heart was beating so rapidly I felt at any moment it would erupt from my chest wall.

We soon arrive at Matron's office. A tall, slim, elegant lady greets us with a warm smile. She is very approachable, and I soon begin to feel more relaxed. She is immaculately dressed in her blue uniform with a frilly hat perched on top of her head. Matron has to meet my parents to discuss my welfare. At that time the age of majority was twenty-one, but nurses often started training at eighteen, so the hospital and Matron had an almost legal guardianship over you throughout your training. My parents were assured that I would be well looked after.

I was used to village life, and had never lived away from home before. Here I was in a strange town not knowing a soul. I didn't appreciate that it was also a big change in my parents' lives.

I am left in the hands of Sister Brooks, the Home Sister. She is a contrast to Matron, a small rotund lady with a very stern face, and an ungainly gait. I feel my stress levels re-emerging as she introduces herself. She escorts me to my room in the nurses' home. Standing with her arms folded under her ample bosom, she informs me of the strict rules and regulations. All student nurses have to live in until they are twenty unless they are married.

My room is bleak and uninviting. The ceiling is high and the walls bland. The small window is so high I have to stand on a chair to see the outside world. The bed, wardrobe and dressing table are in dark wood, the bare floorboards are creaky with a small rug at the side of the bed. In the corner of the room are a washbasin and mirror; bath and toilets are at the end of the corridor. Sister Brooks instructs me to unpack and get dressed in my uniform: she would return shortly to take me to the ward for my first shift. I suddenly feel very alone and apprehensive. I wish my parents were still here.

My cadet uniforms are piled on top of my bed. Unfolding the first one, I can only describe it as resembling a sack, both in style and colour. It doesn't improve with wearing. Its length does not flatter my petite frame. Fully dressed in sack, white starched cap, black stockings and flat, laced, sensible shoes, I anxiously wait for Sister Brooks.

"Hello, have you just arrived?" says a friendly voice. "My name is Betty, I am next door."

"Yes, I am waiting to be taken to the ward," I reply.

"It's a bit scary at first but I'm sure you'll be fine. Sorry, I'll have to go. I'm due back on the ward in ten minutes. Shall I pop in to see you this evening?

"Yes please. I will look forward to it. See you then."

Sister Brooks arrives. "Come along Nurse Clark, I will take you to the ward where you will be working until you start your training." She waddles off down the corridor at speed, with me close behind her.

I am taken to the ear, nose, throat and ophthalmic ward and introduced to Sister Williams, the senior sister. She is a very thin, pale lady who appears to be much stressed. She takes me into the ward where patients are returning from theatre. The majority of them have had their tonsils removed which was a common operation at that time. The smell of vomit and anaesthetic made me feel quite sick. I am to make sure the patients are comfortable, offer sips of water when required and empty the vomit bowls.

A nurse would rush in frequently and check the temperature, pulse rate and blood pressure of the patients. The ward is quiet as most of the patients are sleeping. I feel lost as I watch the other members of staff rushing about. I find the courage to approach Sister and tell her that I can do the patients' observations if it would help, explaining to her that I have completed a two year pre-nursing course.

She checks that I am able to do them accurately, and I am let loose. I feel I am now part of the team and the day becomes more interesting. Staff Nurse asks if I would take a container to the pathology laboratory before going off duty. Walking down the corridor I stupidly become curious about the contents. To my horror, it is an eyeball floating in fluid and it was looking up at me! Fortunately I manage not to drop it. I am relieved when it has been safely deposited in the laboratory.

I feel tired after my shift and happy to be back in my room. Betty soon arrives and we chat until late. She was in the first year of her training, so was able to give me lots of information. We became good friends, but unfortunately our friendship was short lived as she struggled with the examinations and left before I started my training.

# Chapter 3

April had arrived at last. I was settling into hospital life and making new friends. I had worked my last shift as a cadet, and returned my "sacks" to the laundry room. Tomorrow I will be moving to Ellerslie, a large detached house, to start preliminary training.

A motherly figure greets me at the front door. Mrs Gill is in charge of the running of the house. She is a friendly lady with the most beautiful big blue eyes, which appeared to light up when she smiled. She wears her long hair tied back neatly in a bun. She escorts me upstairs, into a large bedroom, which I am to share with three other girls. The room is light, warm and brightly decorated, unlike my room in the nurses' home. I am sure that I will be very comfortable here.

My student nurse uniform for which I had been previously measured is ready for me to try on. Hopefully it will fit better than the sack. It consists of a short-sleeved blue and white check cotton dress and thick belt in the same material. A separate heavily starched white collar is attached to the dress and secured with a button at the back and a stud at the front. A white apron with bib completed the uniform, but has only to be worn while working on the wards and departments.

Mrs Gill instructs me to unpack, dress in my uniform and report to the living room. It takes ages to sort out my uniform and get dressed. It feels very uncomfortable. The collar is heavily starched and starts to chafe my neck, the belt is thick and so stiff it digs into my waist. How was I going to do a physical job dressed like this? I place my pens in my breast pocket and attached my brand new pocket watch onto my uniform with a chain. After straightening the seams of my black nylon stockings and getting into my sensible shoes I am almost ready. The look is completed by folding an oblong piece of white material and holding it in place with a stud. The cap is then placed on my head and secured with white hair grips. At last I am ready; incredibly, the uniform fits well apart from feeling long. It is the 1960s and I am used to wearing a miniskirt. Looking in the mirror I am surprised to see the reflection of a nurse staring back at me.

Nervously I find my way to the living room. Although I am early, three girls have already arrived. Two stand chatting to each other; the third girl is sitting on a settee absorbed in a book. I walk over to her.

"Hi, may I join you? My name is Molly."

"Yes, please do, I am Ann Brown," she replies as she places the book on her knee. I sit down and we instantly get into deep conversation. Ann is a very attractive girl, petite – with short curly dark hair. She looks smart in her uniform. "Have you just arrived?" I ask.

"Yes, I arrived in Huddersfield yesterday and stayed with my parents last night. My sister is a nurse and she has encouraged me to do my general nurse training. As I am in my mid-twenties, I thought I had better get on with it. I live alone so have decided to live in for a while."

The rest of the group gradually arrive, a mixed bunch with a number of girls from Ireland plus two Indian and two Maltese girls. There are around twenty-five students in total and not a male to be seen. At that time, male students have begun entering nursing schools but are still very much in the minority. The Royal College of Nursing formally accepted men into its membership in 1967.

The door opens and three women dressed in uniform enter. The room goes very quiet and we all stand to attention.

"You may all sit down," said the lady dressed in a smart fitted purple dress with a white frilly collar and starched frilly hat on her head. "My name is Miss Hillman; I am the Senior Nurse Tutor. May I also introduce Sister Kershaw and Sister Rhodes who are also Nurse Tutors?"

Miss Hillman continues: "Now you are student nurses, your appearance must be neat and tidy when working in the hospital. Uniform must be worn when attending lessons in PTS. Make-up and jewellery are not permitted and long hair must be tied up neatly."

Introductions followed, each of us giving our names plus some information about ourselves. Following a break we are escorted round the building. In addition to the living room, the main floor has a kitchen with dining room, a practical room and a large classroom.

We enter the classroom, which resembles a schoolroom with lines of desks and chairs. Miss Hillman stands authoritatively in front of the class, while timetables are passed round. "Classes will start at 8. 30am and end at 5pm, Monday to Friday. You will be given a written test on Saturday mornings on the week's lectures, finishing at midday. Some of you may wish to go home, but must return by 10pm on Sunday evening when the front door is locked. Lights must be out by 10. 30pm."

What have I let myself in for? We are all together for lectures which include anatomy and physiology, personal and community health, principles and practice of nursing, psychology applied to nursing, and first aid. We are in small groups for our practical training on the wards.

Lunchtime arrived at last. We form an orderly queue outside the dining room, where we are greeted by Mrs Gill. I sit next to a girl called Linda. She is tall and very thin with pointed facial features. Linda is a very intelligent, ambitious girl who is from a well-to-do family. She has been privately educated and is aiming to become a Nurse Tutor.

The 1960s heralded many changes in the NHS, which has been firmly established and is growing. Nurses are starting to feel more confident and beginning to develop greater independence. Career opportunities are greater than they have previously been. I have no set ambition: at the moment I can't even imagine completing the course.

The food is cooked on site and is delicious – meat, potatoes and vegetables plus sponge and custard. We are all so full, how are we going to concentrate on our afternoon's lectures?

Miss Hillman is already waiting for us when we return to the classroom. Our first lecture is on anatomy and physiology: we are to learn all about the cardiovascular system. I feel very fortunate that I have studied the subject before, and hopefully will not have to concentrate too hard. Miss Hillman starts by describing the anatomy of the heart. I glance at Ann; her eyes appear to have glazed over. Slowly she raises her hand. Miss Hillman stops talking.

"Yes Nurse Brown, what is the problem?"

"I have never studied anatomy before and am finding it difficult to understand, could you go over it again?" she asks. I am amazed at Ann's bravery. The teaching is conducted in a very strict manner, not unlike school; sit, listen, make notes and be afraid to question. But Miss Hillman turns to the blackboard, picks up a piece of chalk and draws a square, then divides it into four small squares to represent the chambers of the heart. She explains the structure of the heart in very clear terms. Ann soon begins to understand. I thoroughly enjoy my first lecture and find the method of teaching very interesting.

"You may go now Nurses; study today's lecture this evening but remember, the heart is a cone-shaped, hollow, muscular organ and not square." She has a sense of humour.

First day over, we all retire to our rooms.

# Chapter 4

On returning to my room, I find that I am sharing with Ann and Linda. A girl called Patricia soon joins us. She is tall, and heavily built, a short curly bob frames her smiling face. I feel sure we will all get along well.

Patricia is in her early twenties and has previously been working as an enrolled nurse. She now hopes to convert her qualification to registered nurse, so will need to complete two years of the course. Enrolled nurses have undergone a two year practical nursing course. They are invaluable within the nursing team, but have few career opportunities.

We are all relieved that the first day is over. The atmosphere in the room is very happy and relaxed as we get to know each other. We are all from different backgrounds and have different personalities, but it seems to make conversation more interesting. Ann has life experience, is mature and very sensible. Linda has had a privileged upbringing, is very posh and well read. She seems to know everything. Patricia comes from a large family, three of her sisters are in the medical profession, and she has got a wealth of nursing experience. I am the youngest of the group and have led a sheltered life, living in a small terraced house with my parents and younger sister. I had grown up in a stable, caring environment. My parents were strict which provided a good foundation for the career I had embarked upon.

"I am worried about the human biology and find it difficult to remember. Could any of you help me if necessary?" asks Ann.

"Just let me know if you are struggling and I will help if I can," I reply. I didn't know what I had let myself in for: biology entailed hours in the classroom staring at the skeleton memorising the detailed structure, naming and describing all the bones in the body.

As instructed we were all in bed by 10pm and lights were out at 10. 30. The chatter and laughter, however, continued into the early hours of the morning. We were all excited and enthusiastic; tomorrow we would start our training proper, a full day of lectures and practical work. I felt contented and less homesick as I drifted off to sleep in my warm comfortable bed.

Woken by the alarm at 7am, we all rolled out of bed, tired and bleary eyed. The day started in regimented fashion, which was to continue at every level throughout training. We had to report down at breakfast by 8am in full uniform. Beds had to be made and our rooms left tidy for inspection.

Following a large cooked breakfast, we attended our morning lectures on personal and community health. Sister Rhodes gave lectures on water purification and sewage disposal. Why did we have to learn this? It seemed so irrelevant to nursing the sick. Was I on the plumbing course by mistake? The day, however, improved as we spent all afternoon in the practical room learning basic nursing procedures.

I didn't realise how much detail went into making a bed, and giving a patient a bed bath. Emphasis was put on the care of patients. They should be in a clean comfortable bed and well-nourished to aid recovery. We practised taking temperatures, blood pressures, and counting pulse and respiratory rates. Preparing injections and injecting an orange was great fun. It proved to be a great bonding exercise, which was valuable experience for when we were working on the wards.

First week over and Saturday morning test completed, I was happy to see Mum and Dad waiting for me. I already felt mentally exhausted and was looking forward to my day off. It was a noisy journey home, I was so excited and didn't stop talking, telling them about the course and the new friends I had made. I had not spoken to my parents since starting PTS: they were not on the telephone at home and the age of the mobile phone was still in the distant future.

Mum and Dad never outwardly showed much emotion but I was aware they were proud of me, and glad that I had settled on the course. Dad was very much the head of the family; he was hard working and a very active person with a variety of interests. He was born in Canada, but while still an infant his Scottish parents returned to their home near Motherwell, where he was brought up. In his twenties he joined the forces as war broke out. He was stationed in Yorkshire where Mum lived. They met at a dance and married in 1942, when Mum was eighteen and Dad was twenty-eight. Dad had been previously married in 1937, and had a daughter, born in 1938 but his wife died in 1939 aged twenty-four of anaemia and cardiac failure. His daughter, Helen, was three years old when they married, and my mum became her step-mum.

Dad rarely spoke of his life before meeting Mum and didn't say much about his war experience either. I remember him once telling me of a bomb hitting below decks when he was sailing to North Africa. He would never forget the screams of the cook as boiling fat spilled over him. Dad was one of the men who volunteered to go down to rescue wounded men.

Mum had been brought up by loving parents with her brother and two sisters. Times were hard and she had worked in the mill after leaving school. She would have liked to have done a hairdressing course, but her parents were unable to afford it at the time. Her extended family all lived locally, and would help and support each other when necessary.

It was good to arrive home, and to see my younger sister Jane. Helen was now married and no longer lived at home. After spending most of my day off visiting friends, resting and sleeping, it was time to return to Ellerslie. Only eleven weeks of PTS were left.

# Chapter 5

Easter Monday soon arrived, but we didn't have a holiday in PTS. It was a glorious spring morning, the air was warm, the sun was shining and the birds sang. How I longed to be on holiday enjoying myself: my brain couldn't retain much more and we had a further nine weeks to endure.

Sister Kershaw must have taken pity on us, as she suggested we sat in the garden to study nutrition. I sat with Ann under the shade of a tree. "Shall we take it in turns to read while the other one relaxes and listens?" she asked. I thought it was a good idea, but not a lot of listening or learning went on that morning. We did however feel well rested.

The rote learning continued, but my respect grew for our senior tutor. Miss Hillman always made her lectures interesting, ensuring that everyone understood. She was very strict with terrific nursing vision, and continued to instil a wealth of education into me and my colleagues throughout PTS.

I was keen to put some of my learning into practice, and was pleased that my placement was on ward 1, a male orthopaedic and general surgical ward, where I would be working a half day each week during PTS. A nurse called Mary Kelly was going to be working on the ward with me. Mary was from Ireland, a tall, slim, pale girl, with long wavy red hair tied up neatly under her cap. She was very quiet and serious, rarely smiled and appeared aloof from the rest of the group.

After adding the starched white apron to our uniform, Sister Rhodes escorted us onto the ward. We walked down a dark corridor; Sister's Office and the kitchen were on the right and two side wards for very ill patients were on the left. Walking through a second door, I was overwhelmed at the sight of the main ward. It was huge. The ceiling was high with tall windows. Rows of neatly made beds stretched down either side. Sister's desk and a wooden medicine cabinet on wheels were in the centre of the ward. The ward definitely had the Florence Nightingale influence. Another door led to an eight bedded annexe, which had patients who were almost ready for discharge.

I felt very nervous and self-conscious walking down the ward and sensed that Mary was feeling the same. We were introduced to the Charge Nurse on duty, which didn't alleviate my nerves. Mr Bates was a small, stocky, middle aged chap with a miserable face. After glaring at us for several minutes, he fortunately referred us to the Junior Sister. Sister Frost was lovely. She was pretty with delicate facial features, and looked immaculate in her pale blue uniform. She was softly spoken and had a gentle manner.

"I know it is frightening when you first arrive on the ward, but you will be fine. You are only here for a few hours today, so I will show you round the ward, and perhaps you can make a few beds before going off duty."

Sister Frost was unlike most of the senior staff. Ward sisters in the 1960s were still incredibly powerful figures. In some cases, trainee nurses were not allowed to speak to them unless they were addressed. There was a lot of respect in the profession for all your seniors, even if they were only one step above you. You didn't even walk through a door in front of somebody more senior than yourself.

Walking down the open ward, Sister Frost continued to put us at ease, but I was aware that we were in full view of all the patients, and some of them were young lads around my age. What would I do if one of them shouted: "Nurse could you help me?" I hope they realise that although I look like a proper nurse in my uniform, I am actually clueless.

We were shown around the ward and became familiar with where things were kept. Sister would frequently stop at a bed and introduce us to a patient; she had such a caring manner. It was clear that she was admired and highly respected. I hope to be like her when I qualify.

There were eight beds left to make. All the staff was too busy to help us, so Mary and I were left to do them. It was like the blind leading the blind. Unfortunately the beds were on the orthopaedic side of the ward and the patients all had broken legs. How do you make a bed neatly around a patient who has only one leg in the bed, the other is tied up in traction? How we struggled, we were so slow. It took us almost two hours to make five of the beds, which certainly didn't look professionally made. It had taken us so long that it enabled us to chat to the patients, which they seemed to appreciate. Apart from their fractured legs, the patients were mostly well, but bored at the length of time they had to spend in bed with their legs in traction. It took around twelve weeks for a fractured femur to heal and eight weeks for a tibia and fibula.

When Sister Frost told us it was time to go off duty, she didn't seem to mind that we hadn't completed our task and said we had done really well. We left the ward on a high and were keen to do our morning shift the following week.

"It is such a lovely day, shall we go into town and have a coffee, then walk back to Ellerslie," I asked Mary. Surprisingly she agreed. Mary seemed more at ease when not in a group – perhaps she was just shy. We were soon in deep conversation. Mary had been brought up in a large family in Ireland. She had four siblings, two sisters and two brothers, who she was missing dreadfully.

"I have never been away from home before, and am feeling so homesick already. I have always wanted to be a nurse but don't think I will be able to cope. There is so much to learn and the girls who I am sharing a room with are not friendly. I feel so lonely," Mary says.

"I am lucky. We all get along really well in our room. Would you like to join us in the evenings? We start studying the day's lectures, but it soon turns to chatter and we usually have a laugh," I reply.

After reassuring her that I am sure the other girls will not mind her joining us, she agrees. We are exhausted by the time we reach Ellerslie. Is this how nurses are meant to feel? Mary met up with us that evening. Fortunately she got along well with the others. Patricia understood how Mary was feeling as she was also a long way from home and missing her family.

We started to enjoy our placement, and we worked well together. Mary seemed happier, she grew in confidence and her personality began to shine.

Although the junior nurses stuck to their jobs, which were more menial such as doing the bedpans, pressure area care, serving meals, feeding patients, cleaning patients' lockers, these were the jobs that gave us a lot of patient contact. Despite the hierarchy, there was a lot of teamwork in the ward. It was long hours of hard graft but everyone knew their role which helped to provide all-round patient care.

Occasionally we were allowed to do more advanced procedures.

"Have you given an injection yet, Nurse Clark?" asked Mr Hicks as he peered down at me. Mr Hicks had recently qualified as a Staff Nurse. He was a frightening individual, well over six feet tall and heavily built. His face was not pleasing to the eye.

"No, I have only injected an orange," I replied.

"When you have finished what you are doing, I will observe you giving Mr Pearce his penicillin injection."

I stood in the treatment room waiting for Mr Hicks to observe me preparing the injection. Penicillin, which had been discovered in 1928 by Alexander Fleming, was a frequently used antibiotic in the 1960s. The first antibiotics were prescribed in the late 1930s, but by the 1950s there was ample evidence of the emergence of resistance. Within four years of penicillin being introduced onto the market, resistant infections were being reported. However, in the 1960s, resistant bacterial strains seemed to matter very little as there was always a new antibiotic being developed to combat them. It was an interesting time to be in the profession; treatments were improving and better drugs were being developed. Nursing practice was also changing as a result of medical advances.

I could hear Mr Hick's heavy footsteps walking towards the treatment room; he stopped on the way to shout at a nurse. He was a bully and I was petrified. *I must do this correctly.*

I checked Mr Pearce's treatment sheet with Mr Hicks: he was due to have 2cc of penicillin given by intramuscular injection. I put on a mask to prevent inhalation of the antibiotic, then thoroughly washed my shaking hands and put on a pair of sterile gloves before drawing the thick fluid from a glass phial into a syringe. I attached another sterile needle to the syringe and placed it in a kidney dish with an alcohol swab to clean the skin.

I was marched down the main ward to find Mr Pearce. He was an elderly gentleman who was suffering from terminal cancer; the penicillin was to treat an infection following surgery. He was a pitiful sight, the curled outline of his painfully thin body visible under the bedclothes. His hands lay on top of the counterpane, his fingers gnarled and covered with transparent skin. His face held a blank expression with eyes that showed no emotion. I had never seen anyone look so poorly, and felt deeply saddened.

"This is Nurse Clark, Mr Pearce. She is going to give your penicillin injection." Mr Hicks then turned to me and ordered me to get some screens to put around the bed. This was a time-consuming chore in itself. The screens were kept at the corners of the ward, on wheels which invariably needed oiling. They had to be dragged, often loudly squeaking, down the ward. I couldn't wait to move to the new hospital where each bed would have its own screens. Mr Pearce rolled onto his side and Mr Hicks helped him to pull his pyjama bottoms down, to expose a mass of bone. Where was I going to put this injection? It had to be put into a muscle and I couldn't see one.

I hated Mr Hicks for putting me in this position – he surely could have found me someone with a bigger bottom for my first injection. I glared at the bottom for a while, drew an imaginary cross on it in my mind so I could locate the upper outer quadrant. This is where I must give the injection to avoid hitting the sciatic nerve. I clean the area with the alcoholic swab and plunge the needle in. I feel sure I have hit the bone. I see a gentler side to Mr Hicks as he shows some compassion as we make Mr Pearce comfortable. At least he treats the patients better than the staff. Mr Pearce looked more relaxed.

"Are you feeling more comfortable now, do you need anything before I leave?" I ask.

"I am fine now, thank you Nurse." It was difficult to understand why he was thanking me, I felt so helpless. I was a nurse, but could not make him well. All I could do was help to alleviate his pain, and try to reassure him.

We were almost at the end of PTS as the four of us sat in our bedroom doing some last minute revision. Several of the girls had already left the course for various reasons: some found the studying difficult, and others were homesick. The rest of us were feeling apprehensive about the examinations which would be over the next two days. We had a practical examination plus lengthy theory examinations to pass. I was dreading the written exams and would be relieved when it was over. The questions had to be answered in essay form, with English and spelling taken into account. We were all so tired; we decided to have an early night and try to get some sleep.

Dawn soon broke on a beautiful summer morning. "I haven't slept a wink," said Ann. "How am I going to concentrate? I am sure to fail these exams."

"I am sure we all feel the same; I have also had a poor night's sleep, my head feels empty and my stomach is churning," I replied. "Hopefully we will feel a bit better after one of Mrs Gill's hearty breakfasts."

We reluctantly filtered into the classroom and sat quietly at our desks. Miss Hillman soon arrived and tried to put us at ease. The papers were given out. We had to sit two examinations that were two-and-a-half hours long and we had to answer all questions. The exam started, the room remained quiet apart from the occasional cough or shuffling of a chair. Typical of the questions asked were:

a) *Name the main branches of the abdominal aorta. How is blood returned from the intestines to the heart?*

b) *What types of muscle are found in the body? Describe the special characteristics of each. Why is exercise important to health?*

c) *Give the composition of air. What impurities may occur in the atmosphere and how are they removed without the aid of man?*

d) *Describe the method of dealing with the waste material from a town house. Why is this important?*

e) *By which routes may drugs be given? Describe how you would administer a dose of a mixture containing iron.*

Time was passing very quickly. I had taken over an hour for the first two questions; I must get a move on with the remaining three.

"Five minutes left, Nurses," said Miss Hillman. I just managed to finish in time. I glanced around; everyone looked very hot and relieved that the first exam was over.

We were all in need of one of Mrs Gill's high calorie meals. We had been fed so well over the past twelve weeks.

"Is anyone else putting on weight? I can hardly fasten my belt and I am sure my boobs have expanded as I am having difficulty fastening my bra," asked Patricia.

"I think we are all putting on weight but don't worry, we will soon lose it when we are working full-time on the wards next week," replied Linda. "I can't believe we have almost finished PTS, we have only got our practical exam this afternoon and our last theory exam tomorrow morning. I have enjoyed living at Ellerslie, and hope the four of us are on the same corridor when we move to the nurses' home."

All exams finished, it is our last night at Ellerslie. We are all shattered and have decided to have an early night. Tomorrow is Friday, our exam results will be given in the morning and we will have the weekend off to recover. We chattered until late that night reflecting on our time spent in PTS. Although it had been very hard work with lots of discipline and no time for relaxation or a social life, we had been well looked after in comfortable surroundings. Linda became tearful, which upset the rest of us. "It is the last night we will share a room together and we have all got on so well together and helped each other. I hope we will remain friends."

"I am sure we will. It will be a big change living in the nurses' home, but we will soon get used to it. We will arrange to get together as often as possible," Ann replied.

Morning soon arrived and we filtered into the classroom for the last time. We had all passed. It was such a happy time – we had been successful in completing the first part of our training. Surely this was the hardest part. I couldn't keep this pace up for three years.

"Well done girls," said Miss Hillman. "I will interview you individually, and then you are free to pack your belongings and leave Ellerslie for a well-deserved weekend. You will return to the nurses' home at the New Infirmary on Monday morning at 9am, where you will be met by Sister Brooks. . . She will show you around the building, and take you to your rooms."

"That will be a treat for everyone; at least I have already met the woman," I whispered to Ann.

Luggage packed, we stood in the doorway waiting for our transport. Dad soon arrived, my personal taxi driver. It should have been a happy time but most of the girls were in tears. We would miss the great camaraderie we had had in PTS. Ann gave me a hug, "Have a good rest and I will meet you on Monday morning."

"You too," I replied as I climbed into the car.

# Chapter 6

It was a large imposing building that stood before me. I had only previously seen photographs of the new hospital, and was overwhelmed by its size and the grounds that surrounded it. I had a terrible sense of direction; how would I manage to find my way around? The nurses' home and school of nursing were in the hospital grounds in a separate building, also very grand and only a short walk to the main hospital building.

The school of nursing has now been incorporated into a "virtual ward" within the University of Huddersfield's School of Human and Health Resources.

I was the first to arrive, as was often the case. Ann soon joined me and it was not long before all our PTS were gathered in the entrance hall. The loud chatter soon quietened to the sound of heavy footsteps coming along the corridor. The vision of Sister Brooks stood in front of us. She was just as miserable as I remembered her. Was she incapable of smiling or was she simply unhappy? She led us down a long corridor into the lecture room.

"Good morning Nurses. I am Sister Brooks, the Home Sister. I will be in charge of you while you live in the nurses' home. Visitors are not allowed in your rooms. The front door is opened at 6. 30am and locked at 10. 30pm. One late pass is allowed per week until 11pm. A book is provided at reception for signing in and out, so we are aware that everyone is in before the door is locked."

My mind started wondering as the rules continued. How are we supposed to remember them all? Do I really want to be a nurse? Most of my friends back home are working weekdays, earning more money than me and having a social life. At last she appeared to have finished telling us what we could and could not do, and we were shown to our rooms.

What a pleasant surprise my room is. Yellow curtains are draped down either side of the large window; the sun streaming in gives my room a bright cheerful feel. Looking out of the window, I can see directly across to the school of nursing section of the building, and beyond it the tennis courts. My room is spacious with modern furniture in light wood. It has a dressing table, a wardrobe with full length mirror, a single bed with shelves at the side for books. A small sink and mirror are in the corner of the room and a beige fitted carpet lay on the floor. What luxury! There are a dozen or so rooms on each corridor, with shared bathrooms and toilets. A kitchen and laundry room are also available.

Unfortunately, Ann, Patricia and Linda were on different corridors, so we arranged to meet to try and familiarise ourselves with the hospital layout. The hospital had first opened its doors in 1965. The wards, however, were still empty, but would be ready to receive patients in the near future. Mary and I will continue to work on ward 1 at the old infirmary until that day arrives.

I was not looking forward to the long working hours with only one day off a week. The shifts would take a while to get used to, in particular the dreaded split shift, where you start at 7. 30am until 1pm, then return at 5pm until 9pm.

Fortunately this shift will be phased out in the near future. I am relieved that Mary is also working an early shift on our first day. Transport will be available to take us back to the old hospital to start our 7. 30am shift. Life will be much easier when the new hospital opens and we can walk a short distance to work. I arrange for Mary to make sure that I am up and dressed in time as I am definitely not a morning person. I don't want to be late on my first day.

# Chapter 7

My first encounter with the operating theatre was in the early days working on ward 1. I was on early shift and had spent the morning in the usual fashion, making beds, wiping locker tops, feeding patients, testing urine samples. It was hard physical graft: I was feeling exhausted and my feet were killing me. I doubted that I had made the correct career choice; surely it was going to get easier.

"Have you been to theatre yet?" Nurse Clark. I was unaware that Mr Hicks was standing behind me in the sluice; his loud voice made me jump.

"No, Mr Hicks," I replied.

Giving me a stern look, he continued. "I would like you to go to theatre with Mr Peters. He is having a minor operation, the removal of a lipoma, which is a tumour composed of fatty tissue. It will be a good first case for you to observe and will enable you to become familiar with the theatre environment. When you have finished cleaning those sputum containers meet me in the treatment room to discuss what you need to do. Mr Peters is expected in theatre in an hour's time." I started shaking with mixed emotions of apprehension, excitement and interest. It would surely be more enjoyable than scraping spit out of containers.

It was common practice, if staffing levels were adequate, for a nurse to escort patients to theatre, observe the operation and care for them on return to the ward. This continuity of care enabled the patient to feel more relaxed.

The last sputum container dealt with, I met Mr Hicks in the treatment room. My role in theatre was discussed, Mr Hicks stressing that I must not touch anything while in theatre as it was a sterile environment.

Mr Peters had been admitted the previous day and would have a short hospital stay. He was a tall, distinguished man of around sixty, with a pleasant face and a full head of white wavy hair. He was a proper gentleman, very well spoken, and didn't seem in the least bit nervous. It might be him trying to put me at ease, although I didn't let him know it is my first time in theatre. I felt we would get along well.

A jolly porter soon arrived and I helped Mr Peters to shuffle onto the trolley. We had a good chat on our journey to theatre and soon arrived in the anaesthetic room, which made me feel quite light headed. Fortunately I was taken into the changing room by one of the theatre nurses and instructed to change into one of the short sleeved V-necked dresses. They all looked huge. I rummaged through them in an attempt to find a small size but was unsuccessful. Dressed in a larger version of my cadet sack, I put white plimsolls on my feet, concealed all my hair under an unflattering cap and placed a mask over my nose and mouth. This was definitely not a good look. I was provided with a locker for my uniform, but couldn't wait to get it back on. I would wear my uniform with pride from now on and would forgive it for being so uncomfortable.

The theatre seemed very large and bright with a tranquil atmosphere. Staff were moving about and quietly chatting to each other with only their eyes visible. The faint clanging of instruments could be heard as they were placed on a trolley ready for the procedure. Surgical instruments were kept in large cupboards in theatre and were sterilised on site in large autoclaves.

Staff had to memorise the names of the instruments and know what was required for each surgical procedure, so the correct instruments were selected and autoclaved prior to each operation. Gauze was also sterilised on site, using steam heat in an autoclave. Life would be much easier in the New Hospital, with a Central Sterilising Department responsible for sterilising all equipment in the hospital.

I watched the surgeon intently as he scrubbed his hands and arms up to his elbows with a soapy brown solution. It seemed to take ages. He put his arms through the long sleeves of his gown without touching any part of the outside. A nurse then tied the back of his gown and opened a packet of sterile gloves, which he again put on only touching the inside. I would have to learn the technique, but guess it will take a lot of practice.

I stood quietly with my hands out of the way behind my back and observed the procedure. Fortunately it was very quick and not gory. Lipoma cut out, stitches and dressing in place, the procedure was complete. I felt relieved that I had not vomited and had managed to remain upright. Mr Peters was soon returned to the ward and made comfortable in his bed. He would hopefully be discharged home the following day.

I was the first one in our PTS to have experience in the operating theatre and couldn't wait to tell everyone about it. I had found the experience interesting but did not want to work permanently in the theatre environment. I enjoyed chatting to the patients too much.

The ward was very busy and I was an hour late getting off duty. I was tired and hungry, so called in the dining room on the way back to the nurses' home to have a bite to eat. As usual I had a high calorie meal to replace my energy. It was almost 7pm when I arrived back in my room. I found the strength to make myself a cup of tea, kicked off my shoes and lay on top of the bed to read a book. I was woken to the sound of leaves rustling and rain pattering against my window. It took a while for me to realise where I was. It was 5. 30 in the morning and I was still lying on top of the bed, fully dressed in my uniform. A whole cup of cold tea was by the side of the bed and my book had fallen on the floor. I was on duty again at 7. 30am, so better get up and find the strength to do it all again.

# Chapter 8

Any doubts about nursing being the career I wanted were dispelled soon after meeting Michael. It was another early shift on the ward. Listening to the report given by the Night Staff Nurse, I found it difficult to comprehend what had happened to Michael. He had been admitted the previous night having sustained multiple injuries in a horrendous car accident. He had been in theatre for hours prior to being moved to the ward in the early hours of the morning. The list of injuries included fractured arm, ribs and pelvis, severe injury to leg, lacerations to face, and groin injury; the list seemed endless. The vision in my mind did not prepare me for the emotional effect on seeing Michael for the first time.

As usual I was doing the mundane junior jobs that day, but was also required to help with Michael's care. He was being nursed in the side ward opposite Sister's office. He was lying motionless in bed, eyes closed, with lines of pain etched on his forehead, skin waxen and bloodstained, short blond hair dishevelled. A plaster cast was visible on his arm. A blood drip and urinary catheter were in place. He was only seventeen years old. My body went numb. I felt deeply upset and found difficulty holding the tears back. How had this happened, and would he ever be well again? It was going to be a long road to recovery for him.

It took four nurses to move him while two of us changed his bottom sheet. Lifting equipment was not available as it is today, so nurses were taught various lifting techniques – back problems were common for nursing staff. I will never forget the screams of pain as Michael was moved, despite the powerful pain relief he had been given.

Several weeks later Michael was moved to the main ward. He was improving slowly but remained in considerable pain. It was good to see his personality emerging as he chatted to the other lads on the ward. He had an outgoing personality with a good sense of humour. Although he was depressed at times, he remained positive about his future. I enjoyed helping with his care; he was always very appreciative and my job was becoming worthwhile.

I was nearing the end of my working days on the ward and was thrilled to be working a full day with Sister Frost. Our duties included injections, medicine round and the full care of Michael. He required a bed bath and his wounds had to be dressed which exhausted him. He was due to be given an injection of morphine prior to us starting his care. This would hopefully make it less painful for him.

Drugs like morphine are kept under strict legal control by the Dangerous Drugs Act (DDA); others like barbiturates are under slightly less rigid legal control by the Pharmacy and Poisons Act. All these drugs must be kept in a locked cupboard and the DDA drugs must be kept in a second locked cupboard within the main one.

The nurse in charge of the ward, who must be State Registered, keeps the keys to the cupboard and is responsible for all the drugs. She must keep a record of the number and kinds of drugs under her charge and must record any drug that is given out. Each time a drug is given to a patient it must be signed out by the nurse in charge and witnessed by another nurse. This ensures these drugs are kept safely.

Sister Frost, like the majority of senior nurses, was dedicated to the job. She was soon to be married, which had previously been a taboo in the profession; but married sisters were now tolerated. She took such pride in her work and was an excellent teacher. Following the strict procedure of checking and documenting the morphine, Sister Frost watched me give the injection. I was amazed how quickly Michael became relaxed and pain free.

I was very impressed how Sister Frost cared for Michael, nothing was rushed. She had a wonderful serenity about her which calmed him. We bathed him and made him comfortable. I was allowed to dress his leg wound which took ages. It was such a deep wound it had to be packed with ribbon gauze soaked in eusol antiseptic solution to encourage healing. It was thought he might have had to have his lower leg amputated but fortunately the wound was now healing slowly.

Michael looked so comfortable when we had finished his care. I had thoroughly enjoyed my day with Sister Frost, and she had taught me so much. I had come to know Michael well and had become very fond of him. He was recovering remarkably well, but would remain in hospital for many months. Fifty years ago hospitals were much more personal than they are today. Patients stayed in hospital for much longer and nurses really got to know them as people with lives outside the hospital.

I was nearing the end of my time on the ward. I had enjoyed the teamwork, but not all the staff had been approachable. One such person was the most senior Sister on the ward who was a formidable character. I had never been introduced to her and had rarely seen her. She was short in stature and round like a ball and wore a white frilly lace hat tied underneath her chin. Like most of the senior Sisters she was a spinster who had been dedicated to the job. Nowadays she rarely emerged from her office and looked well past retirement age.

The only occasion she had cause to communicate with me was during Matron's daily ward round. The patients had finished their lunch and were in bed, quietly behaving. Sister and Matron had just entered the ward. I was at the top of the ward with another nurse, collecting the dirty crockery and cutlery. It was so quiet you could have heard a pin drop until I accidentally tripped, sliding to the ground with plates, cups and cutlery clattering on the wooden floor. Sister folded her arms and in a loud voice shouted down the ward, "Nurse, try not to be so clumsy." I could hear the young lads tittering, but I felt very embarrassed and upset. She was definitely one person I would not miss.

I felt sad to be leaving the ward, but excited that I would soon be working in the New Infirmary.

# Chapter 9

I enjoyed going home on my days off. Our house was near the top in a long terrace of houses. The road outside was cobbled. You entered the house immediately into the front room, which was the posh room of the house. It had a piano, black and white television, three-piece suite, and Mum's treasured display cabinet.

Mum took great pride in keeping the room immaculate. She would spend hours polishing the green tiles which surrounded the fireplace, so you could see your reflection in them. The room was mainly used for special occasions such as Christmas and birthday parties. This room led into the kitchen which was the hub of the house. There, we would either be enjoying a meal round the dining table or sitting on one of the comfortable chairs at the side of the fireplace, reading or catching up with the local gossip.

Mum always seemed to be busy cooking, baking, washing and ironing which all went on in the kitchen. Between the two rooms were steep stairs leading to two bedrooms, and a bathroom.

My sister Jane and I shared the back bedroom which overlooked Dad's garden, his pride and joy. It was a large garden full of the most beautiful flowers with a vegetable patch at the top. In the summer months Dad would sell bunches of his flowers to the villagers. As a young child I would deliver them for him to earn some spending money.

At the top of the garden there had been a piggery which Dad had adapted into a garage. In the distance we could see the local church spire. The gate at the top of the garden led onto a short country lane, which led up to the primary school. When I attended the school, Mum would listen for the bell to ring and I could run up the lane and be on time for lessons. Mum and Dad had the front bedroom which overlooked the street. There was not much motor traffic but it was noisier than our bedroom with the early morning milkman, delivery vans selling bread, fish and tea, plus the occasional rag and bone man with his horse and cart collecting everything you put outside the front door, clothes and old furniture being common items. It became even noisier at night as the Friendly Inn was near the bottom on the opposite side of the street. Late at night people could be heard leaving the pub, shouting to each other as they attempted to stagger home.

Apart from a small, plug-in electric fire, our only source of heating was by coal fire. We were allowed to set the coal fire from an early age; I enjoyed rolling the newspaper for the first layer, then piling on the sticks before putting the coal on the top. There were also fireplaces in the bedrooms, and a fire might be lit if one of us was ill in bed.

It was freezing in the winter. If it was cold and frosty, icicles would form inside the windows. If it was raining heavily the roof would leak and water would drip through our bedroom ceiling. A bucket was placed on the carpet to keep it dry. The coalman would deliver along the street, tipping coal from the outside through the trap door into the cellar. It was good to huddle round the fire on a cold winter's night.

It was a busy household, always full of life. Most of Mum's extended family lived nearby and often visited. My maternal grandmother had been a large part of all our lives until her death when I was sixteen years old. She had lived on the opposite side of the street and was sadly missed. Her house was a one-up, one-down with a steep stone staircase and a small pantry. She only had an outside toilet, which was round the corner from her house. You had to take your own toilet paper or use the squares of old newspaper strung on a nail. She had played a major role in my upbringing and was such a character.

Grandma had only two of her teeth left, they looked rotten and not very stable, but she refused to have a set of dentures. It didn't, however, seem to hinder her; she frequently walked to the fish and chip shop in the evenings, taking our order if needed, and call in our house on her way home to enjoy her fish supper.

Life at home was so different to my new life in Huddersfield. It was escapism from all the stresses in the hospital environment. I very rarely had a weekend off so didn't get much opportunity to see my old friends. I frequently seemed to have Mondays off. The entire street washed on a Monday. The gardens were full of activity. Weather permitting, clothes were hung out on the long washing lines to dry. The neighbours would have a good natter as they went about their work. Many of them had known me since I had been born and were very interested to know about my nursing course. If it was raining, the wet clothes were put on the wooden clothes rack and hoisted up to the ceiling to dry. The kitchen would often smell like a launderette for days.

It was such a close-knit community in the village: nothing seemed to move on. I had done Mum's shopping in the local shops on a Saturday morning up to leaving home. Some of the neighbours asked if I would also do their shopping, and the number of shopping lists grew quickly. It took ages, chatting to the shopkeepers, but the money I received from the neighbours for doing their shopping boosted my income.

The local GP held his surgery in rented rooms in a large detached house. No appointment was necessary; you just sat in the front lounge and waited for your turn. If you were ill on Saturday morning, a surgery was held in the back room of the cobbler's shop. Customers would come into the shop with shoes for repair, while patients sat discussing their ailments, waiting to see the doctor. It was like a social gathering.

I was living in two very different worlds and it felt confusing. At times I didn't feel I belonged in either. Village life, in many ways, seemed to be stuck in the austere nineteen-fifties; the hardship of the post-war times still lingered on and prevented people from enjoying the nation's re-birth. Britain was entering an age of heady optimism and there was a feeling that anything was possible.

It was the decade of the greatest contrasts and a good time to be a teenager. We no longer had to dress like our mothers, but could develop as individuals. We were able to think for ourselves and have a say in how we dressed. The miniskirts I wore often earned my parents' disapproval. Some were so short you had to bend at the knees rather than bend over. It was the swinging sixties and for many was about rock'n'roll and sexual liberation. The biggest thing that would change women's lives was the contraceptive pill, which first became available in 1961. Other significant advances in this decade included the legislation of abortion in 1967.

So my new life in Huddersfield was vibrant and exciting. It was a magical time and I was happy. I was enjoying my job, my confidence was building and I was making lots of new friends. My social life was improving, with the odd shopping spree and evening out to the cinema or the pub. Finance proved to be a problem as we only earned £11 per month plus keep. I would usually spend it by the middle of the month, borrow money from my dad and repay him on my next pay day. Mum was very encouraging. She would frequently remind me that nursing was a vocation, and if I worked hard, I would eventually earn a decent salary and not have to borrow money from Dad.

# Chapter 10

I woke early on the morning of September 22nd 1966 following a restless night's sleep. It was the day we had all been waiting for and I felt very excited at the thought of working in a brand new hospital. It would be very different to the outdated Old Infirmary.

In the 1960s, hospital premises were considered to be increasingly outdated, which had led to Enoch Powell's hospital plan in 1962. This was a ten year programme to develop district general hospitals for population areas of around 125,000.

I was on late shift on the female medical ward, so had plenty of time to walk around the hospital grounds to see what was happening. The atmosphere was electric. A fleet of ambulances brought in-patients from the Old Infirmary building. Numerous agencies were on hand to ensure a smooth transition, including the Local Defence Corps who set up a two-way radio link between the two hospitals. There was intense activity but everything seemed to be moving smoothly.

Fully dressed in my clean, well starched uniform and with plenty of time to spare I set off for work. Most of my friends were on early shift so I felt very alone. On the way I met a group of excited nurses also on late shift. Unfortunately none of them was on the same ward as me. We went into the hospital via the side entrance, walked past the staff dining room and along a dark, cold, basement corridor. We all piled into the lifts which took us up to the wards.

I was early for my shift, so I popped into the staff cloakroom, which was situated outside the ward, to check my appearance again. The ward was breathtakingly light and spacious. Two sections of the ward were open plan, joined by a long corridor, with side wards on one side and the nurses' station and kitchen on the other.

The hospital had lots of innovative features and was the first in the country to install a new type of patients' bedside locker incorporating nurse-call communication and radio systems. When a patient pressed the call button it would also light up at the nurses' station, which was more convenient than shouting for a nurse.

The atmosphere was surprisingly calm and organised. I introduced myself to Sister Bell who was the Ward Sister, a tall lady with bird-like features and a drainpipe figure and a reputation of being very strict. She was standing at the trolley serving dinner for the patients. Meal times were a very important part of the day. Fortunately I had missed the bedpan and hand washing round which was routine prior to all meal times.

I joined the nurses round the trolley to help give out meals and help patients who were not able to feed themselves. We had to report back to sister if patients didn't eat their food, as sufficient nourishment was important in helping recovery.

Screaming and the sound of plates and cutlery clattering onto the floor could be heard coming from one of the side wards. A nurse appeared in the doorway covered in food and looking far from pleased.

"Edith is refusing to eat any food and has become very aggressive," she said to Sister Bell.

"Go and clean yourself up, Nurse. Staff Nurse will come to assist you; Edith has to eat, she has had her insulin injection," she replied abruptly.

During the report, I learned that Edith was an insulin dependent diabetic. She was an elderly lady who lived alone. Her diabetes was very unstable, and she had been admitted several days ago in a coma. She was often very confused and aggressive towards the staff. Being the most junior nurse on the ward, how long would it be before I was given the job of feeding her?

The basic routine work was much the same as it had been back on ward1, although it felt easier with all the modern equipment. I was relieved to see each bed had its own screens and they weren't on wheels. Patients had their own thermometers, each thermometer resting in pink fluid in a glass container which was attached to the wall. Oxygen was also piped to each bed, each patient having their own oxygen mask if needed.

The routine work for the junior nurse was easier on the late shift as most of the beds had been made; I had made so many that I must have perfected the art by now. Bed baths and dressings had usually been completed and urine samples tested by lunchtime.

Pressure area care was an important part of patient care, and was routine day and night. Patients tended to spend much longer confined to bed in those days. These patients would have their pressure areas treated twice daily (bottom of the back, shoulder blades, heels and any other parts of the body subject to pressure owing to their position). These areas were massaged with soapy water and rinsed with clear water, dried and rubbed with spirit and powder. The treatment was carried out at least at four hourly intervals if the patient was emaciated, oedematous, helpless, paralysed or incontinent.

Helpless patients were not allowed to lie more than two hours in the same posture. "Beds and backs" was frequently a job given to the junior nurses and didn't do their hands any favours; unfortunately hand cream was not provided for the staff.

I soon began to enjoy my time on the ward and became interested in the medical conditions and their treatments. I would spend hours with my head in my *Toohey's Medicine for Nurses*, reading about diseases the patients on the ward were suffering from. It helped me to retain the information. I was fascinated by all the different drugs.

I was particularly interested in nursing patients with heart disease. Lots of patients on the ward had suffered coronary thrombosis, which is the common cause of a heart attack. Unlike these days where patients are soon out of bed and moving about, patients had absolute rest; everything had to be done for them. In severe attacks even so slight a strain as turning in bed or reaching out for a drink from an awkwardly situated bedside locker could prove too much for a badly damaged heart. The length of time kept in bed varied according to the severity of the attack and the extent to which the heart recovers. Three weeks may be long enough in mild cases; in severe cases where there is shock or heart failure, six to eight weeks may be necessary. Patients then spent a week or two sitting in a chair and a similar time walking around their room or ward. A convalescent holiday is then needed before returning to work. If the initial attack was severe, patients were unable to go back to work of a strenuous nature.

Diet had to be light as a heavy meal could throw too great a strain on the heart. Patients were often prescribed a diet restricting saturated fats and reducing carbohydrates and sugar, and this diet was the cause of lots of complaints.

I hadn't had a day off for ten days, but was happy to be working with Staff Nurse Clegg this morning. She was an experienced nurse who appeared to be brilliant at just about everything. She glowed, she had a magnetic quality about her and everybody seemed to like her. She was such a happy individual who was always smiling.

Glancing at the work list I soon realised the day I had been dreading had arrived; it included Edith's care, and feeding her would definitely be my job. Edith peered at us through her thick rimmed spectacles as we entered the side ward. She was a small, plump lady with pale skin and a mop of grey tightly permed hair. She seemed relatively calm, but on talking to her it soon became evident that she was slightly confused.

"Edith has not been eating properly which has caused her blood sugar level to fall too low. We need to observe her closely for signs of hypoglycaemia, which is low blood sugar. The signs could be mental confusion, vacant expression, sweating with a rapid pulse, palpitations, and trembling. We need to check her urine three times daily for sugar. Would you try to get a specimen of urine from her before lunch and we will check it together?" asked Nurse Clegg with a smile on her face.

Edith was surprisingly compliant and an ample specimen was soon obtained. In the sluice, Nurse Clegg watched as I placed five drops of urine from a standard dropper into a clean test-tube plus ten drops of water. I then dropped a clinitest reagent tablet into the test-tube and waited for a boiling reaction to take place. Fifteen seconds after boiling had ceased I shook the tube and waited. The fluid changes colour, turning green, orange or dark brown according to the amount of sugar present. If sugar is not present the fluid remains blue. Her urine showed a trace of sugar. The clinistix test, a quicker method of testing urine for glucose was now available, but was unsuitable for the diabetic patient as it did not show the amount of sugar present. A clinistix strip was simply dipped into the urine, the moistened end turning blue in about a minute if sugar was present.

"We need to give Edith her insulin injection before lunch. I will show you how to prepare the injection and you can give it. You will need to enter it on her drug chart, not forgetting to enter her urine test results on the appropriate chart as well," my mentor continued. "I would like you to give Edith her lunch. It is not an easy task but it is important that she eats as much of her lunch as possible, so try your best."

I was imagining being covered in food and having plates and cutlery thrown at me, not to mention the verbal abuse Edith was capable of giving out. I reluctantly followed Nurse Clegg into the treatment room.

"Have you much knowledge on insulin and the various types?" As I had only limited knowledge, she continued, "Edith has soluble insulin prior to meals. When it is injected subcutaneously it leads to a fall in blood sugar, but its effect only lasts a few hours. Various forms of insulin have been prepared which prolong its action to last all day. The long acting ones that you will frequently come across are Insulin zinc suspension which lasts all day and Protamine zinc insulin which is very successful when added to soluble insulin. Let me show you how to draw the insulin up into the syringe."

I was trying to concentrate but it seemed a lot of information to retain. How did she remember all this? If I felt confused already, it was about to get much worse.

"Insulin is prepared in solutions of forty or 80 units per mil. A standard insulin syringe has twenty marks per mil." She handed the syringe to me to look at as she was explaining. I was unsure whether or not it was helping me to understand.

She continued. "If forty strength insulin is used, each mark on the syringe is worth two units. If eighty strength insulin is used, each mark is worth four units." Nurse Clegg looked at me and started to laugh. "I know it sounds complicated but the more you do the easier it gets. It is important that you always get insulin checked prior to giving it, even if you are a qualified nurse as it is very easy to make a mistake. Unfortunately, many syringes with different marking systems are available and can lead to considerable confusion."

Fortunately it became a little clearer in my mind as I prepared the injection but would take a lot more practice before perfecting the skill.

"It is important to vary the injection site from day to day. Sites suitable are upper arm, stomach and thigh. We need to also document where we have given the injection," explained Nurse Clegg as we walked down the corridor towards Edith's room.

Edith was sitting up in bed as we entered. She peered at us in her usual fashion but appeared rather vacant. Fortunately her last injection had been given in her thigh; it was definitely the easier option to give it in her arm. Apart from the verbal aggression she did at least keep still. I was not looking forward to the final hurdle, the dreaded feeding.

Sister Bell carefully weighed Edith's food before putting it on the plate. This was common practice at the time to ensure that the diabetic patient got an adequate amount of protein and carbohydrate, plus fruit and vegetables. I was instructed to get her to eat as much as possible as the tray was handed to me. My uniform was clean as I entered the room, but I wondered how long it would remain that way. Edith glared at me initially, and then surprisingly a big smile appeared.

"Hello Denise, it's lovely to see you. Has your mother come with you?" she asked.

I didn't know who Denise was but clearly Edith liked her and was pleased that she was visiting. I decided to play along and take the part of Denise.

Sitting next to Edith's bed I explained that I was alone as Mum was busy. "I have brought you some lunch and thought I would help you to eat it."

I continued to engage her in conversation as I fed her which seemed to distract her from the fact that she was eating. "Have you noticed my new budgie, Denise?" she asked. "I got him last week and he is already saying a few words. Go over and talk to him if you like."

I walked over to the corner of the room to talk to the imaginary budgie, hoping that nobody would enter the room. Edith's conversation with Denise continued to flow and soon she had finished her lunch. "I will have to go now Edith as Mum is expecting me home," I told her.

"It has been lovely to see you Denise, call again soon if you can," she shouted as I left.

Relieved that she had remained confused while eating her lunch, I walked down the corridor with a tray containing empty plates and my uniform was still clean. I never told anyone my secret, but of course after that I was frequently given the task of feeding her. The Denise role worked every time, which must have added to the good report I received on leaving the ward.

# Chapter 11

The corridor outside my room had quietened down at last. It was my day off, but as I had been invited to go out with a group of nurses tonight, I had decided to stay in the nurses' home and put the day to good use. It was the first day off when I hadn't gone home and it felt very strange.

I was woken early to the sound of alarm clocks ringing, music playing and nurses clattering about noisily getting ready for work. Unable to go back to sleep, I decided to get up and do some washing as it would be a week before I would have the use of Mum's washing machine. I soon discovered that washing clothes in the nurses' home was a laborious task. As we didn't have a washing machine, it had to be done by hand. Fortunately we were provided with a dryer, iron and ironing board. I had never seen a Flatley clothes dryer before, though it was a very popular piece of electrical equipment in the sixties. It was a free standing white cabinet. Inside it had an open heating element at the bottom which consisted of zig-zags of coiled wire; at the top were removable wooden slats. Damp clothes were placed over these slats, and with its lid still off, it was plugged into the electrical supply. You had to be very careful how you draped clothes over the slats, because if anything fell onto the heating wire there would be a fire. 'It would not pass the health and safety regulations today.

After placing my hand-washed clothes in the dryer and switching it on, all I needed to do was frequently check the drying process and make sure my clothes hadn't been incinerated. But I couldn't believe my eyes when checking the dryer for the third time: all my underwear had gone! It hadn't dropped into the dryer so it must have been taken. Surely someone was playing a joke? My underwear was never seen again and I spent weeks looking at nurses of a similar size to myself and wondering if they were wearing my knickers and bras. I always took my washing home after that experience.

The rest of the day was more fruitful. I managed to catch up on some studying and tidy my room. I was beginning to enjoy life in the nurses' home, although, as in the hospital, the rules were very strict. We had to keep our rooms clean and tidy, beds had to be made and sheets changed weekly. A cleaner would clean the basin, dust around, and vacuum the carpet on a regular basis.

We were also responsible for our uniforms, and had to put our dirty uniforms in a brown container each week, to be collected and taken to the laundry room for washing and starching. If we were lucky our container arrived back several days later full of clean uniforms. Occasionally they went missing and you would be running out of uniforms before they were located. Most commonly someone had picked up the wrong container or it hadn't left the laundry room.

Visitors were not allowed in our rooms. On one occasion I was visiting the toilet late at night, when I was met by a young man running down the corridor followed by a policeman. This rule was obviously not for everyone.

The rule that had to be broken was the one late pass we were allowed each week, which was only until 11pm. I was going to try out the night life of Huddersfield for the first time and as some of my friends were working until nine, we wouldn't be returning until the early hours of the following morning. I was to meet two of my friends in the television room at 10pm.

It was very exciting getting ready for the unknown. What would my parents think if they knew what I was up to? Following an indulgent hot bath with Fenjal bath oil, I slipped out of the bath and started to get ready. Face made-up, hair back-combed and stiffly lacquered, dressed in minidress and high heeled shoes, plus a squirt of Estee Lauder Youth Dew, I was ready. Glancing in the mirror I barely recognised myself; it was usually a sensible looking nurse that looked back at me.

Fortunately, the warden was nowhere to be seen and the television room was dark and empty. Soon Sue and Carol arrived and we sneaked out of the door unseen, not having signed out. They had arranged for the fire escape door to be opened so we could get back in. It was all very exciting, but looking back I realise what an irresponsible thing it was to do. What if there had been a fire while we were out? Being teenagers I don't even think that entered our heads.

Chattering and giggling we climbed onto the top deck of the bus. None of us was aware of the cold October evening and we were definitely not suitably dressed for it. We soon found ourselves in front of the large door of Lord Jim's disco. Sue banged loudly on the door; a small flap was opened and two large brown eyes glared at us before letting us in. The place was alive with loud music and groups of young people dancing, chatting and drinking. What had I been missing? This was surely going to make the long working hours and studying in our own time easier to bear.

Hours later, in a drunken state with blistered feet and thumping heads, we all fell into a taxi to take us back to the hospital. The fire escape door was open. We all crept quietly back to our rooms. Thankfully I was on a late shift the following day, but couldn't wait to hit the high spots again.

# Chapter 12

The morning had been hectic with the usual shortage of staff, too many duties and insufficient time to complete them. Everything seemed so rushed, I had already managed to break two glass thermometers on the temperature round. I was working on the male ear, nose and throat ward. Fortunately I'd had no problems settling into the routine, as the senior staff were the same as on the ENT ward at the Old Infirmary. Sadly, Sister Williams was on long term sick leave suffering from a mental breakdown. Her replacement was Sister Newton, newly promoted and enjoying her new found power. She was a tall, fat individual, who today would be classed as clinically obese. She thrived on giving orders, never encouraging or praising junior staff for their efforts. Thank goodness Nellie, the indispensable ward maid, was still around. She had worked on ENT for many years and always knew the up-to-date gossip. She was trustworthy and you could rely on her discretion if needed.

It was my first experience of admitting a patient on my own: little indeed did I know of the challenging task ahead. Bill was a dingy, drab, miserable little man, who was suffering from deafness. He looked much older than his sixty-two years. The colour of his long hair was indeterminate beneath the filth; it had obviously not been washed for many months. His skin was grey and deeply lined. His nails were long, thick and filthy, and his teeth resembled brown pegs. The smell was putrid. Bill (he insisted that we called him by his Christian name) spoke in a soft voice and gave me very little eye contact. He lived alone and had been severely neglecting himself; understandably, he rarely smiled.

Taking his medical history and filling in the relevant forms was the easy part. How was I going to clean him up and make him presentable? The bathroom had to be the first port of call. It took a lot of persuasion to get Bill to remove his clothes and climb into the warm bath I had prepared for him. It took ages to clean his skin and hair, but he did seem to eventually enjoy the experience. Dressed in a pair of hospital pyjamas, he was beginning to look human again. A manicure and pedicure were all that was needed to complete the new look. His teeth, however, were beyond my capabilities – definitely a job for the dentist. Bill seemed pleased with his make-over, in particular his short, clean fingernails.

Bill was suffering from otosclerosis (abnormal bone growth around the stapes bone, one of the tiny bones in the middle ear) which was causing his hearing loss. He had been admitted for a stapedectomy, an operation to by-pass the diseased bone with a prosthetic device that allows sound waves to pass to the middle ear.

The operation was a big success. His change in personality was unbelievable; he became very sociable and never stopped talking. Whenever he saw me, he would shout me over to have a chat and show me his clean fingernails. . I felt guilty at the revulsion I had felt on first meeting Bill.

His wife, who he had been devoted to, had sadly died several years previously. They had been unable to have children, and the rest of his relatives didn't want anything to do with him. Fortunately, he had a kindly neighbour, who would help with his shopping. He had obviously become depressed and coupled with his hearing loss had let himself get into that appalling state.

Bill looked very smart on discharge. I observed the discharge procedure with interest. I had been nursing patients in hospital without thinking about the environment into which they would be discharged. A social worker had been organised to visit him at home. Hopefully outings would be arranged for him and he would get help with his cleaning and cooking. I never saw Bill again, but often thought about him and hoped his life had improved.

One of the requirements of nurse training was the completion of the *Record of Practical Instruction and Experience for the Certificate of General Nursing*. It was a brown booklet which the Ward Sister or Nurse Tutor had to complete. One stroke in the appropriate column signified that we had been instructed in the procedure, a cross indicated that we were proficient. Mr Boothman was suffering from cancer of the neck which was affecting his breathing by pressing on his airway. He had a tracheostomy, a surgically created opening in the neck leading into the trachea (breathing tube) to by-pass the obstruction, which was preventing oxygen reaching his lungs. It is maintained open with a hollow metal tube held in place by tapes that tie around the neck. The tube can be connected to an oxygen supply and ventilator to assist breathing. An inner tube needs to be removed for cleaning when necessary. It was under the critical eye of Sister Kershaw that I was to change the tube. Mr Boothman, although only in his late fifties, looked frail and tired. Despite being in considerable discomfort and having difficulty communicating due to his tracheostomy, he tried to remain jolly. I hadn't met Sister Kershaw since PTS, but remembered how high her standards were. She promptly arrived in her immaculate starched uniform ready for business. I had to do this correctly!

Although I found her rather intimidating, she had a surprisingly good bedside manner which instantly put our patient at ease. Mr Boothman was sat up in bed, relieved to see us. He appeared to be in a lot of discomfort. The inner tube sounded to be full of mucous so I quickly washed my hands, put on sterile gloves and a mask and suctioned the mucous out of the tube. Strangely, although I found mucous quite repulsive, I enjoyed listening to the sound it made as it was sucked out of the tube and seeing the instant relief on the patient's face.

The bed was surrounded with equipment which included a tray containing a sterile inner tube. I changed the tube easily and Sister Kershaw added a cross to my brown booklet. Following that day, every time I encountered Mr Boothman, he would give me a Mars bar. I hadn't the heart to tell him that I didn't like chocolate; I just gracefully accepted them. Fortunately my family did like them, so none was wasted.

One Sunday evening near the end of my placement, when Sister Newton was in charge, I was working the late shift with Mary Kelly who had recently started working on the ward. It was good to be working with Mary again and catch up with what was happening with some of the other girls from PTS. We were all so busy working long unsociable hours that we rarely got the opportunity to see each other. "I hope we will get off duty on time as we are up to date with the work and the ward is quiet. I am going out this evening and don't want to be late meeting my friend," Mary said.

*She must be aware of the fire escape procedure* I thought. I barely started to reply when Sister could be heard shouting for us. We quickly responded.

"What is left to do, Nurses?" she enquired. Feeling very pleased with ourselves, we informed her that all the work was up to date. She continued, "Well done. You have half-an-hour left before the end of your shift, so I would like you to collect a urine sample from each patient, test it and report your findings to me."

We were not pleased as we gave a urinal to each patient and asked them to hurry up and give us a specimen. "I've just had a pee, Nurse, and can't be expected to do another yet," was the response of one of the patients? "Why do we have to?" asked another.

"Sister has told us we have to test everyone's urine before we go off duty and I am going out at nine-thirty. My friend will be worried if I don't turn up on time. So hurry up," Mary replied abruptly.

"Why don't we test the specimens that we collect and make the rest up? We can always say the made-up ones were clear. I'm sure the patients will say they have provided a specimen if she asks them," I suggested. We stuck to the plan, although the majority of the patients squeezed out a few drops for us when aware of the situation. We were late off duty that evening. Mary's friend had waited in the cold and was beginning to worry as she arrived. Sister Newton never commented on the results of our urine testing.

It was a privilege to be working in the New Infirmary, which was said to be one of the most modern hospitals in the country at the time. Standards were very high on every ward and department. The strict routine was very similar on each ward. You could walk on any ward at lunchtime and the scene would be the same: nurses standing around the electric food trolley which was plugged into the mains keeping the food hot. Sister would serve the patients' dinners onto hot plates, which nurses would take on a tray and feed the patient if necessary. It was a time consuming job for all the nursing staff, but a vital part of nursing care. It was probably a relic of the old days when many of the patients were chronically malnourished so their dietary needs were of utmost importance to enable them to recover. It is unbelievable that today in our modern society there are so many reports of poor quality hospital food. Hygiene standards were high; we were made aware of the prevention of cross-infection. We were frequently washing hands, before and after each procedure. Patients were also encouraged to wash their hands before meals and after going to the toilet. Bedridden patients were provided with soap and a bowl of water. When patients were discharged it was the nurse's job to wash the mattress and bed frame, and re-make it with clean linen. Nurses removed their aprons when leaving the ward to help prevent spread of infection. The ward maids tended to work on one ward, and took great pride in keeping it spotlessly clean. Nellie was always busy, rushing about with a damp cloth or sweeping brush in her hand, chatting and laughing with the patients. She was clearly very happy in her role. Visiting times were restricted: evening visiting only, plus afternoon visiting at weekends. Only two visitors were allowed at each bed which must have helped to reduce the amount of infection being brought into the hospital. Chairs were provided and visitors were not allowed to sit on the bed. We walked around frequently to ensure nobody was breaking the rule. MRSA had not yet been heard of, probably due to hygiene standards, restricted visiting, plus the non-abuse of antibiotics.

Matron or her assistant would do a daily round on each ward and department. The standard on the wards had to be kept high as we never knew what time she would arrive and she noticed everything. She would do a full ward round with Sister, making sure patients were comfortable and happy with their care, but her eyes and ears didn't miss a thing.

"Go and put a clean apron on Nurse. . . ."

"Slow down Nurse, Nurses do not run. . . . . ."

"Could you help this patient to sit up, Nurse?" It did all seem trivial compared to the work we were expected to do, but it was standards.

A key development was the Salmon Report of 1966, as the nursing times reported at the time. It recommended a change to the senior nursing structure and effectively heralded the end of the traditional matron role. The report proposed that each hospital should have a chief nursing officer reporting to hospital management, and a hierarchy of principal nursing officers, senior nursing officers, nursing officers and ward sisters or charge nurses. Although the end of matron was resisted by many in nursing at the time, the recommendations of the report also aimed to raise the profile of the profession in hospital management and ensure senior nurses gained access to management training. The Salmon Report was a shake-up of a regime that had been there for many years. There would be no central person in charge of the standard of nursing care, and many of the staff in charge would be administrators who needn't necessarily have had nursing or hospital experience. Fortunately, Matron remained in charge of the hospital throughout my training.

As a junior, I lived in fear of the doctors: they seemed so important. A Consultant's round was quite a spectacle. All patients had to be in a clean bed, professionally made, the sheets tucked in with neat envelope corners. Bedside lockers had to be tidy and all aligned. I often wondered if the Consultant noticed all the effort that had been put in before his arrival. Sister did the round and would often take a senior nurse with her. Junior nurses were often banished to the sluice or treatment room to do some cleaning, keeping them out of the way. The Consultant would arrive in his smart suit, followed by his Registrar and Housemen in white coats. Female doctors were rarely seen as it was very much a male dominated profession. A dietician and physiotherapist would often join the group. Patients' records were stored in a metal cabinet, which Sister would push around the ward, handing the Consultant the appropriate record and discussing the patient's progress. It took ages, but we enjoyed our time in the sluice having a natter and doing the minimum cleaning.

What huge responsibility was put on nurses! Most tended to be very young when starting training, often coming straight from school, their only experience being in the classroom. We were expected to look after very sick and dying patients, but the majority of my colleagues seemed to be full of enthusiasm and vitality with an inexhaustible capacity for laughter. I found this quite amazing given the nature of the work. Perhaps it was the only way to cope with the job.

# Chapter 13

I was greeted by the bitterly cold night air as I left the nurses' home. We were in the depths of winter. The snowflakes had stopped falling, the clouds had disappeared and the stars twinkled brightly, their reflection glistening on the ground. A heavy frost had descended in all its beauty, covering my path to the hospital. I was alone; the only sound to be heard was the crunching of the frozen snow under my footsteps. I shivered, but was thankful of my thick woollen black cape with its bright red lining.

My thoughts were fleeting as I hurried towards the hospital for my first night duty. *What was I doing with my life? Saturday evening 8pm and I was going to work; shouldn't I be out with my friends enjoying myself?* It was a strange feeling, still only eighteen years old but expected to do the work of a mature person. My uniform made me feel very special and I felt great pride in wearing it. It transformed the fun-loving teenager into a responsible nurse, and I felt like an actress taking on a new role.

Despite the heavily starched collar and thick belt, I felt more comfortable and had more freedom of movement when wearing my uniform. This was probably due to the introduction of the pantyhose (known today as tights). It liberated women from girdles, roll-ons and suspender belts. Tights were easy and comfortable to wear, especially with miniskirts, as there was protection from the elements and no unsightly glimpse of stocking tops. Stocking tops were never visible under our long uniforms anyway, but tights were so comfortable in comparison.

Some of the girls from PTS were also working their first night. We had arranged to meet in the coffee lounge before starting work. Hopefully we will have the same lunch break to enable us to catch-up with each other.

I was surprised to hear that Patricia had left several weeks ago. She was apparently finding the course difficult and was having family problems. Our numbers were quickly diminishing. How many would be left at the end of the three years? I hadn't seen Ann and Linda for ages so we had lots of gossip to catch up on. Ann remained very enthusiastic, always looking on the bright side. Linda was very quiet and not her usual confident self. Mary was extremely happy, very different from when I had first met her in PTS.

We had each packed a small bag containing toiletries, so we could freshen up before starting the following morning's routine work, plus books to do some studying if possible. Ann's bag was the largest, containing additional bits, including a novel and her knitting. She was obviously banking on a quiet night.

There was an indescribable quietness as we walked along the corridor to start our nine weeks on night duty. I was working on the medical paediatric ward, Ann was on surgical paediatric, Linda was on female surgical and Mary was on male medical. We will definitely have a variety of patients to discuss when we meet up.

Apart from the occasional cough or cry, the ward seemed very quiet and organised. Other than experience at Seacroft Children's Hospital while doing my pre-nursing course,

I hadn't much knowledge about children and it wasn't a placement I had been looking forward to. I was working with Staff Nurse June Cummings, who gave me a warm smile as we stood waiting for Sister Dixon to give us the ward report. On night duty, senior student nurses were also left in charge of the wards. It was a huge responsibility for a student nurse, but provided good experience for when you qualified. All wards were overseen by the night sisters who would do a full ward round each night and would be available if there were any problems. Sister Dixon was a very serious individual; it was difficult to imagine her enjoying herself or having a laugh. She appeared quite elderly through the eyes of an eighteen-year-old but was probably around her early fifties. She had worked on the ward for many years. Listening to the report, it was obvious that she was very efficient and dedicated to her work.

All the day staff had gone and it was time to start the evening routine. Staff Nurse gave me a list of jobs to do, while she did the more complicated procedures. The ward was busy but without the frantic rush of the adult wards. I was busy feeding and changing babies, and settling them down to sleep, which I did find relaxing. Staff Nurse was not at all officious; she left me to do my work and offered help if I needed it. Hygiene was of upmost importance. A white gown was worn over our uniform when treating patients. A different gown was worn for each patient to help prevent cross-infection. Infection could be spread very quickly, especially given all the gastroenteritis that was around at the time. There were all sorts of conditions on the ward. Several patients had been admitted with pyrexia of unknown origin (PUO); they had a high temperature, but the cause was unknown. Such cases would rarely be admitted to hospital today. We had to monitor their temperature four hourly; usually it soon returned to normal and they were discharged home.

Richard was a terminally ill baby who was not expected to live much longer. His parents had been at his bedside for several days and nights and were supported by the nursing staff. It was such a pitiful sight to see his mum gently cradling him in her arms with tears streaming down her cheeks. I had seen lots of terminal illness and death in the adult wards, but was finding this particularly difficult to cope with.

Although hospital visiting remained restricted, much needed changes were taking place. About two generations ago little was done to support children or parents when children were in hospital. From the sixties onwards, advances in hospital architecture demanded that hospitals shift from open wards to semi-private and private rooms, so it became impossible for the hospital staff to keep an eye on all patients simultaneously. Such changes meant that parents could pitch in and give their children the non-medical but essential comfort they needed. Nowadays across the nation, at just about any time of night or day, you are likely to see parents visiting their sick children. These days it seems so obvious that seriously ill children need their parents beside them.

It was 11. 30 and most of the patients were settled and the lights were dimmed. My body clock was telling me that I should be in bed; it was going to be a long night. Sister Jones the Night Sister arrived to do the ward round with Staff Nurse. Thank goodness you had to be in your second year before you went through the ordeal. Sister Jones was a tall slim lady with a straight back and long neck. She held her head to one side and reminded me of a swan. She walked with a gliding motion and had a natural attitude of authority and grace. Before leaving the ward she said to me, "Nurse Clark, as it is your first night I will send a member of staff to help you when Staff Nurse goes for her break. You must bleep me if you have any concerns." I hadn't considered Staff Nurse taking her break and leaving me alone on the ward. My friends were already in the dining room when I arrived on my break and were all looking worse for wear. I didn't feel hungry, but as I needed to keep my energy levels up to survive the night, I grabbed a snack.

"I don't know how I am going to stay awake all night and remain alert," said Linda, as she tried to stifle a yawn.

"I feel the same. Fortunately the ward is very busy, so I haven't had time to realise how dreadful I feel. I could fall asleep now I have sat down. I thought patients slept during the night to enable us to have a rest!" replied Mary.

Ann looked as bright as ever and was her usual happy self. "I must be lucky. Most of the babies and children are settled and fast asleep. It has been theatre day today; I think some of them are still under the effect of the anaesthetic. I have even managed to do a few lines of my knitting."

I continued the conversation. "I can see across to your ward and have been watching you at the nurses' station with your knitting. Life is so unfair. Who are you working with?"

"Angela Smith. She is a third year and has worked on the ward for several weeks. She is very efficient and well organised. Now the patients are settled we take it in turns to check on them and do the observations. No doubt it will all change when we start the morning routine," Ann continued.

"Has anyone seen Linda? I thought she would be down for a break. I thought she appeared rather quiet when we met earlier."

We had all noticed how quiet and unhappy Linda was when we had met and we were concerned.

"Perhaps we ought to ask her if things are okay when we see her. She is usually so full of life," I said "She might just be feeling exhausted like the rest of us, and the thought of our exams in three months doesn't help matters. Well girls, I had better move or Staff Nurse Cummings won't be pleased." I stood up and the rest reluctantly followed.

Back on the ward, Staff Nurse was busy preparing for an admission. Baby Darren was due to arrive within the next hour. He had been vomiting for a few days and was losing weight; it was thought he may have gastroenteritis.

"I am just popping down to the dining room for a quick bite," she said "Nurse Peel is going to help you while I am away. I should be back before Darren arrives. If not, ring the dining room and they will inform me. Don't worry, you will be fine. There is plenty of support around." She hurried off the ward.

I was busy admitting baby Darren when Staff Nurse returned. Darren was two months old and didn't look at all well. He was very pale and shrivelled with a worried expression on his face. His eyes were sunken and he was very dehydrated. He appeared hungry, loudly exercising his lungs. He was feeding well but projectile vomited after every feed. The doctor soon arrived and diagnosed pyloric stenosis, the narrowing of a passage in the stomach. We tried to reassure his young parents who were very anxious and tired. The doctor sat with them and explained that the condition was congenital, and occurs in infants from four to seven weeks old, usually males and first babies, which was the case with Darren. He explained that Darren would require a minor operation to divide the fibres of the muscle which guards the opening of the stomach. This would stop the vomiting and Darren should soon return to full health. Darren's parents seemed more relaxed as Staff Nurse explained that he would be transferred to the surgical ward and would have his operation in the morning.

"Nurse Clark, could you ring the surgical ward and inform them that we will be transferring Darren over to them shortly. Briefly tell them of his condition and diagnosis, and that he is first on the list for surgery today. I will give them more information when I go across to the ward with him." I was thrilled at the request as Ann was still sitting at the nurses' station. She would have to put her knitting down and do some work! Several days later Ann informed me that Darren's surgery had been successful. He was now feeding well, had stopped vomiting and was plumping up. His parents were relieved that he was almost ready to be discharged home.

By this time it was 4am. I had never felt so tired. My brain felt like cotton wool and I was experiencing difficulty stringing a sentence together. How was I going to cope for another four hours? I just wanted to sit down and cry. I had another six nights to work before I had any leave. It was torture. Surely, you must get used to working at night, or why would people choose to do it? Perhaps I just need to keep busy and take my mind off how dreadful I feel.

A ringing sound alerted me away from my thoughts. It was coming from Richard's side ward. As I approached,

I could see his father holding onto the door frame, uncontrollably sobbing. His mum was rocking in the chair holding Richard's lifeless body. A feeling of helplessness came over me. I couldn't begin to imagine the grief his parents were going through.

Richard looked peaceful as I helped Staff Nurse to wash and dress him in a white gown. She was very gentle as she handled him and took such care. It had been a difficult first night, both physically and mentally.

It was a beautiful winter's day as I left the hospital. The air was fresh; the sky was bright blue and a carpet of fresh snow lay on the ground. I felt so tired my legs could hardly move. The emotional shock of the night's work must have contributed to my fatigue.

Somehow the nine weeks flew by and I gained lots of experience. Staff Nurse had allowed me to give medicines and injections under her supervision. I had learned new skills like passing a tube through the baby's mouth into the stomach to wash it out, and how to give subcutaneous saline where the saline is injected under the skin to help keep the baby hydrated.

But I had found it thoroughly exhausting. Sleeping during the day had proved to be difficult due to the general noise of the nurses' home coupled with the light streaming through the bright yellow curtains. I tried to catch up on my sleep on my days off at home. On one occasion, I had travelled home straight after finishing my night shift. Unable to stay awake beyond lunchtime, I decided to have a few hours' sleep. The next thing that I remember was being woken in the evening by Mum, to tell me that dinner was ready. I couldn't believe it when I realised it was dinner time the following evening.

I had slept solidly for around thirty hours! I looked pale and tired, and had lost a lot of weight as I hadn't been able to eat properly while on nights.

Understandably my parents were very concerned about my health. Mum looked after me, making sure I had plenty of rest and nutritious food. My paternal grandmother helped to increase my calorie intake. She had a baking day on Thursdays; I enjoyed visiting her to see what she had made. The wonderful smell would waft towards me as I entered the house; the kitchen was full of freshly baked scones, bread, pies, cakes and biscuits. I often wondered who was going to eat it all as she lived alone. I would leave with a bag full of food guaranteed to put some of my weight back on.

# Chapter 14

The year had started well with the excitement of the official opening of the hospital by the Prime Minister, Harold Wilson, on 27th January 1967. I felt relieved that I had completed my first night duty, and was near the end of my first year of training. Fortunately the next six weeks would be spent in our first year study block. I was looking forward to seeing everyone, although our numbers were continuing to dwindle. I was aware that I looked dreadful and was a shadow of my former self, but felt proud that I had managed to last so long. Six weeks spent in the classroom plus regular breaks and time to eat a good lunch should soon have me feeling well again.

Following the initial three months PTS, in addition to long hours of hard work on the wards, nurse education consisted of study blocks of six weeks in each of the three years. Classes would run from 9am until 4. 30pm, and then we would continue to study in the evening. At the end of this first study block we would sit our Preliminary State Examinations, which had to be passed before progressing into the second year. If you failed you were allowed to re-sit the exam, but we were all keen to pass first time and go into our second year. I had recently had my nineteenth birthday and couldn't wait to get a blue stripe on my white cap to show that I had been promoted to a second year student nurse.

We were excited as we walked down the corridor to the classroom, all smartly dressed in uniform. The classroom was similar to the one at Ellerslie with rows of desks and chairs. The room was bright and cheerful. Spring was round the corner and it was a lovely sunny day. The flowers could be seen through the large windows, their buds opening to expose the most beautiful colours.

Ann had arrived first. She was sitting at the front desk reading a text book.

"Are you trying to catch up with your studying after spending all that time knitting your jumper?" I questioned, sitting next to her. She grinned in response. Linda and Mary sat behind us and the chatter started. It felt good to be spending six weeks together but we all missed Patricia plus the other girls who had left the course. We felt relaxed as a group; it was respite from working on the wards.

Ann was her usual self, full of energy, and never stopped talking. She always managed to cheer me up as well as exhaust me. Mary was such an interesting person; she continued to be homesick at times but would frequently communicate with her family by letter. Fortunately she would be going home for a holiday following our examinations. Our concerns for Linda grew. She was withdrawn, deeply unhappy, and reluctant to socialise with us despite our encouragement. It was obvious she didn't want to discuss her problems with us.

The noise gradually got louder and louder as more students filtered into the room. The laughter was a tonic. We were all amazed that we had survived the first year and had so many experiences to share with each other. The three tutors arrived, the room went instantly quiet and we all stood to attention. It was good to see we hadn't forgotten the discipline!

We all fell back into learning mode without any problems. I particularly enjoyed the practical classes, and the teamwork it encouraged while working together. I frequently volunteered to take the role of the patient, because I was easy to lift and move about the bed. We practised bandaging on each other and learned more difficult dressing techniques. In preparation for our second year, we had to learn how to set trays and trolleys for more advanced procedures.

"We are going to learn how to set trays for urinary catheterisation and passing a Ryle's tube this morning," Sister Rhodes informed us one day.

I had not observed either of the procedures, although I had helped to nurse patients who had them in place. Surely she wouldn't want a volunteer for the demonstration, would she?

The tray for catheterisation consisted of a sterile catheter, sterile gloves, kidney dish, swabs, forceps, needle and syringe and sterile water. Sister Rhodes went through the procedure for female catheterisation which seemed very complicated. "Thoroughly wash hands before putting on gloves. When the patient is in the correct position, with knees drawn up and legs flopped apart, gently swab around the vulva. Take the catheter out of the packet and locate the urethra. This can be difficult to find in some females and it is possible to push the tube into the vagina instead. Push the tube into the urethra; when urine comes out, the tube is in the bladder. If the catheter is to be left in, the indwelling catheter (often referred to as a Foley catheter) is held in the bladder by a water-filled balloon which prevents it falling out. These catheters need to be changed regularly, and often have to be clamped and released periodically so the patient doesn't lose bladder control." My head was full of information which didn't make much sense. How was I going to be able to do that to a patient? It seemed a huge responsibility.

Sister Rhodes must have observed all the blank expressions and let us have a short coffee break before confusing us even further. Fortunately I found the passing of a Ryle's tube easier to understand. "A Ryle's tube is pushed up the patient's nostril and down into the stomach; it can be used as preparation for gastric surgery, to give feeds or to obtain specimens of stomach contents." We gather round to observe the contents of the tray. It contained the tube, kidney dish, bowl, lubricant, syringe, litmus paper and cotton wool balls.

"Reassure the patient and explain what you are going to do. Firstly examine the nostrils. Many patients have one nostril bigger than the other, and it is advisable to choose the larger one," she said.

Ann looked at me, rolled her eyes and we both started tittering. "We will have a look later," Ann said.

The instruction continued. "Clean the nostrils, then look at the patient and try to imagine approximately where the stomach will be, so you have an idea how much of the catheter you will need to push down. You will need a longer length of catheter for a tall person than a small one. Lubricate the end of the catheter and push into the nostril until some resistance is felt, then ask the patient to swallow while the tube slides down into the stomach.

"Sips of water can be offered to the patient if this helps the tube go down. To check the tube is in the stomach, attach the syringe to the end of the tube, withdraw some fluid and test with litmus paper. The litmus paper should turn red as stomach contents are acid. This is very important, making sure the tube is not in the lungs, although this would likely cause the patient to cough."

The room went very quiet as we were asked if there were any questions. Sister Rhodes looked at our dazed faces, smiled and reassuringly said, "Don't worry, I appreciate it is a lot of information to take in. Once you have observed the procedures on patients it will become much clearer, and it will become second nature when you have practised a few."

Most of us were rather anxious at the thought of having to do such things to patients. Perhaps second year was not going to be any easier with all this added responsibility. It hadn't bothered Ann at all, as she said, "Well, I gather by the information given, that in both procedures, you can either get the tube in the right or the wrong hole and you just have to remember to check that you are in the right one." Ann had such a calming influence on us all. She was able to think logically and was confident in her practical abilities. It was a few months into my second year before I practised the procedures. Surprisingly I found catheterisation relatively easy. I was soon able to do it efficiently, causing the patient minimal discomfort. Passing a Ryle's tube, however, was a different story. This was definitely not an easy procedure, and took lots of practice to perfect. The first one that I attempted to pass was on an elderly gentleman prior to him going to theatre. He was sat up in bed reluctantly waiting to swallow the tube.

I managed to push the tube up his larger nostril until I felt some resistance. Now should come the easy bit, while the patient swallows the tube slides down into the stomach. The poor guy was swallowing as I had to push on the tube, still feeling some resistance. It certainly wasn't sliding anywhere. He became distressed as he started to gag and his eyes started to water. What was I doing wrong? If the tube was in his lungs, surely he would be coughing by now. Staff Nurse, who was watching, quickly stepped in. She obviously knew what had happened. The tube was nowhere near his stomach – it was coming out through his mouth. We had not been warned that this might happen. The patient, fortunately, was very understanding and forgave me.

The enjoyable practical lessons were such a contrast to some of the lectures. Full day's lectures could be very boring and often left me feeling mentally exhausted. I would often find myself doodling on scraps of paper, or looking out of the window and daydreaming.

One such morning, feeling particularly bored in a personal and community health lecture, I was relieved when lunchtime arrived. The four of us eagerly left the classroom. As we were walking down the corridor, I happened to glance out of the window which looked directly across to the nurses' home. I could hardly believe my eyes. In one of the rooms I could see Norah, the cleaner, apparently looking in a drawer. Norah had been a cleaner in the hospital for many years. She was a small, plump lady who walked with a limp and spoke with a strong Irish accent. She was very sociable and popular with the nurses. Why was she going through someone's personal belongings? She seemed so trustworthy. The others soon joined me to ask what was wrong.

"That's my room," said Mary, looking shocked. "What is she doing? She will only find clothes in those drawers and they are no good to her. She would never get into them! I lock my valuables in the wardrobe."

"Are you going to go and have a word with her?" asked Ann.

"Don't know yet, I will think about it over lunch."

After further discussion we decided that if nothing was missing, she could consider putting a note in each drawer indicating that she knew her drawers had been rifled. Fortunately nothing had been taken, so we concluded that Norah was just being nosey.

We all enjoyed the study block and being able to spend time together. After only a year of nursing there were many experiences to share, and we learnt a lot from each other. It was extremely hard work but we did a lot of studying in our small group in the evenings. Ann, Mary and Linda would frequently join me in my room: I think the attraction was the goodies I brought back from Grandma; we had lots of breaks to eat cakes and biscuits. The sugar rush helped us to concentrate until late at night. Linda was becoming less of a concern – she was more sociable and relaxed, though it was obvious she was not enjoying nursing.

It was such a relief when the dreaded examinations were completed. We now had two weeks' annual leave in which to recover, before hopefully going into second year. All four of us had holidays organised with our families. My caravan holiday with my parents and sister was very enjoyable. Sitting in the warm sunshine, going for leisurely walks, and swimming in the sea made me feel much better. But the thought of the examination results, which would be out during the second week of the holiday, were constantly on my mind.

I was unable to wait until I returned home to learn my fate, so found a public telephone box, lifted the big black receiver, put my money in the slot and dialled the hospital's number. "Huddersfield Royal Infirmary, how may I help you?" said a friendly voice. I shakily pressed the A button, and asked to be put through to the school of nursing.

I had passed! I quickly pressed the B button to get my change, and ran back to the caravan to tell my parents the good news. The relief was indescribable; I could hardly believe it: I would be a second year nurse with a blue stripe on my hat!

# Chapter 15

It was a warm summer day travelling back to Huddersfield in "Dad's taxi". The scenery was so colourful, with the trees turning various shades of green and the flowers providing a blanket of vivid colour. I felt well following my holiday. My batteries had been re-charged and I had managed to put on some weight. My next placement was on a male medical ward but unfortunately it was night duty again, and I had only just recovered from the last lot! Staring out of the car window, I reflected back to the first time I had made this journey on that cold, miserable day. I had been seventeen years old, lonely, nervous and apprehensive and totally unaware what I had let myself in for. Just over a year later, I am feeling very different. I am becoming a confident nurse. I felt excited at the thought of returning to start my second year and not be at the bottom of the pile any longer. The junior nurses would now show me some respect, and I would be able to join the other second year students in the dining room. Mum and Dad were now getting used to taking me back to the hospital, but I still sensed a hint of sadness as I waved goodbye to them. After taking my belongings up to my room, I hurriedly made my way across to the coffee lounge where I was meeting my friends. Through the smoke I could see that the three of them had arrived.

The coffee lounge was far from a healthy place to meet; in the 1960s smoking was fashionable with the nursing and medical staff. Although none of our little group smoked, we must have inhaled lots of second-hand smoke. Several of the students had sadly failed their exams, but thankfully my friends had passed. They were all on day duty so I wouldn't see much of them for a while. Following lots of chatter, I left to catch up on some sleep as I started work that evening.

I was wakened to the sound of my alarm clock, amazed that I had managed a few hours' sleep. I had plenty of time to have a good dinner which hopefully would help me to cope with the night's work.

It was a bright sunny evening as I strolled across to the hospital. Groups of nurses were also going to start their shifts. It always surprised me how happy most of them were, even when going to start a night shift. It certainly wasn't my idea of fun.

The ward was a hive of activity. On arrival I was met by Christine Pendle, a third year student, whose reputation of being very lazy went before her. She was a very serious individual with a monotone voice. She moved very slowly and didn't look capable of doing much work.

We took the evening report from Junior Sister Bennett who had been promoted. She was enchanting. I couldn't take my eyes off her and found difficulty concentrating on the words coming out of her mouth. She was a beautiful redhead, her hair a mass of thick curls. She had fragile facial features, slightly freckled porcelain skin and bright blue eyes. She had perfect slender fingers and manicured nails. I was intrigued while watching the expressive movement of her hands which almost spoke for themselves. I was completely confused when the report was finished, although I had made some notes there was so much to take in. As there were just the two of us working on the ward, I soon came to realise that I was still the junior nurse having to do all the mundane jobs. I certainly couldn't imagine Pendle giving me any help.

First step was the kitchen, to get the trolley ready for the evening drinks. The patients were served with a milky drink to help them sleep or tea if they preferred. I stood waiting for the milk to warm, hoping that nobody would ask for Horlicks as I was unable to mix it without lumps floating on the top. Hopefully Ovaltine would be more popular.

"Hello Nurse. I am Mr James, one of the long stay patients. I don't believe we have met; are you new to the ward?"

I turned to observe a slim, middle aged man, his black hair speckled with grey. He had such a friendly face and wonderful smile that I immediately warmed to him.

"Yes it is my first night on an adult ward. I have just started my second year but still feel clueless," I replied.

Mr James smiled. His breathing was laboured as he spoke. "I am sure you will soon get used to things. The patients are a nice lot and shouldn't give you too much grief. Would you like me to do the night drinks? I will collect the cups and do the washing up as well if you like. I have done it many times before and it will allow you to get on with your nursing jobs."

It was an offer I couldn't refuse. Patient participation sounded a good idea to me. Off he went with the trolley and I could hear him chatting and laughing with the patients as I started the observations, in which I was now well practised and able to do at speed.

Temperature, pulse rate, respiration and blood pressure were taken with unsophisticated equipment in those days. The mercury glass thermometer required approximately three minutes to achieve a stable reading. The pulse rate was monitored by counting; the nurse would locate the radial pulse at the patient's wrist, place her first and second fingers over the pulse and count for one minute. Respiration was counted by discretely observing the patient's chest rising.

Blood pressure could take a lot of practice before it was mastered. A mercury sphygmomanometer and stethoscope were required. A cuff was placed around the upper arm and inflated until the artery was completely occluded. You would place the stethoscope over the artery and listen as the cuff was slowly released, while observing the height of the column of mercury in the sphygmomanometer. As the pressure fell a pounding sound was heard, noted and recorded as the systolic blood pressure. The cuff was further released until the sound was no longer heard, which gave the diastolic blood pressure. Today these observations are recorded electronically, providing greater accuracy and efficiency in reading.

I soon managed to complete my work. The patients seemed friendly, most of them happy to exchange a few pleasantries. The majority of them were suffering from chest related illnesses, mostly caused by cigarette smoking. They were frequently caught having a sneaky cigarette during the night. I found it difficult to comprehend that Mr James was suffering from terminal lung cancer; he appeared so well apart from his difficulty with breathing.

Once all the patients were settled down, Mr James made us a pot of tea and the two of us had a short break and chat about the patients and their care. Christine had worked on the ward for a while, so she knew the patients well and I felt that we would get along fine.

The night turned out to be exceptionally busy. In addition to all the care the patients required, we had two deaths and an admission. Neither of us was able to have a break, but fortunately managed to get a couple of sandwiches sent up from the canteen, and Mr James, who had difficulty sleeping, had made us endless cups of tea.

It had seemed a short night as dawn broke: early morning and the sun was soon shining. Mr James was dishing out cups of tea to the patients. Christine and I had started the morning routine, washing the very ill patients and making their beds, providing bedridden patients with a urinal and bowl of warm water, helping them to wash if necessary, doing the medicine round, giving injections, doing observations, checking drips. In addition, the senior nurse had to write a report on each patient plus a report on the very ill patients for Matron. It was a huge amount of work for two people to get through. Dreamily walking back to the nurses' home, I heard footsteps close behind me.

"It is Molly, isn't it?" I heard a voice say. I turned round to find myself face to face with Barbara Peacock, fully dressed in uniform. I was sure I wasn't dreaming as I would recognise that cheeky grin anywhere. She was a larger than life character who you couldn't help but like. I had met Barbara several years before when I worked at Seacroft Children's Hospital as a pre-nursing student. Barbara was a pupil nurse doing her Enrolled nurse training.

"Hi Barbara, this is a surprise, I can hardly believe it. What are you doing here?" I replied.

"I finished my Enrolled nurse training and fancied a change, so decided to do the conversion course as job prospects are much better for Registered nurses. I fancied this new hospital after working in such an old one. How long have you been here? Are you enjoying it? What is the social life like?"

"You haven't changed a bit; trust you to ask about the social life. I remember you being a party animal. We must arrange to meet and have a catch-up when I can think straight."

Barbara was also on night duty. She was on the corridor below mine so it would be convenient to meet before going on duty. My social life took an upward turn after meeting Barbara. We were able to spend lots of time together while we were working similar shifts, and started to play hard as well as work hard. I was now spending some of my nights off in Huddersfield. Barbara and I had started going out together, mostly to the pub where she would drink lager or vodka and lime, and I would drink Babycham or Cherry B. Barbara loved socialising and would attract people when we were out – not surprisingly, often members of the opposite sex. She was definitely a man magnet, and we had plenty of dates in those weeks, although she had a steady boyfriend back home. We often met in Barbara's room to get ready and decide where we were going. It reflected her laid back personality: everywhere was cluttered. Shoes and clothes covered a large area of the floor, the bed was covered in books, and dirty cups and plates with dried food on them were strewn around the room. I found it fascinating watching her carefully apply her make-up, starting with pale foundation, then emphasising her eyes with kohl, black mascara and false eyelashes until she resembled a panda. Fortunately her lipstick was a pale pink. Her clothes were always brightly coloured and her skirts very short.

Although there wasn't a distinct shoe look in the sixties, slip-on shoes with clunky heels were popular plus go-go boots which were a must-have to wear with miniskirts and came in every height imaginable. Barbara, however, preferred her brightly coloured stiletto shoes on which she would happily totter around. I felt rather drab in comparison and desperately needed something new to wear. The shops in Huddersfield had a wide variety of colourful clothes to choose from, enabling me to brighten up my image. It was a decade of sweeping change throughout the fashion world generating ideas and images which still appear modern today.

Sister Brooks had now moved onto my corridor and she didn't miss a thing. During my night duty, sleeping had become impossible. The days were becoming warm and very sunny. The yellow curtains didn't help matters. In desperation I put a piece of black material up at the window to keep out the light. It made all the difference, enabling me to sleep without any problem. To my amazement it lasted several days before Sister Brooks noticed it. Drifting off to sleep one morning, there was a loud thumping at my door.

"Open this door at once, Nurse." Half asleep I opened the door, to see the unwelcome vision of Sister Brooks. She was standing with her arms folded defensively under her bosom, and she was looking furious. "Take that down from the window immediately," she demanded. "It looks awful from the outside."

I decided to stand up to her. What could she do if I refused? "If I take it down I will be unable to sleep and will be unfit for work tonight. If you are able to find me a dark, quiet room to sleep in I will gladly move, otherwise it stays." She glared at me, turned and left in a huff. She never mentioned it again and the blackout remained. Night duty was going well. I was sleeping much better and managing to eat well with the added help of Grandma's goodies. Barbara had introduced me to a social life which was a much needed outlet from work. I felt and looked better than I had done in ages. We had only another week left on night duty and were planning a night out at Lord Jim's disco at the end of it.

Mr James wasn't looking at all well. He was very pale and thin, his eyes sunken. You could sense the sadness behind his smile. I will never forget the evening he met me in the kitchen to apologise that he was unable to do the drinks. He was in a wheelchair, too weak to stand and could barely speak, but was sorry that he couldn't help me. With a lump in my throat and holding back the tears, I wheeled him back to bed. Over the next few nights his condition rapidly deteriorated. He was given morphine for his severe pain. His wife visited frequently during the day, but Mr James insisted she went home at night to get some sleep. He was such a considerate man.

The night he died will always remain in my mind. He was suffering the most dreadful pain despite his medication. It was a quiet night on the ward, so Nurse Pendle suggested that I sit with him for a while. We chatted about his family and his daughter whom he obviously adored. He told me that she was soon to be married. "Do you think I will be well enough to walk her down the aisle?" he asked.

I thought for a while before replying. He must have realised that he was dying. Why was he asking me this? What could I say?

"I am sure you will. Let's just concentrate on getting you well," I eventually replied.

He thanked me, smiled and fell into a peaceful sleep. It was the early hours of the morning, but we felt Mrs James must be informed of her husband's condition. As Mrs James didn't have a telephone at home, we had to contact the local police station and ask them to ask her to return to the hospital. He slipped into a coma and died peacefully with his wife sitting by his bed.

I was distraught. I ran into the sluice, unable to hide my emotions – not at all the way a professional nurse should conduct herself. I was crying uncontrollably, unable to stop the tears streaming down my face. Nurse Pendle soon joined me and gently put her arm around me.

We discussed Mr James and she fully understood how I was feeling. "I feel terrible that I lied to him, saying he would be well enough to walk his daughter down the aisle," I said.

She looked at me sympathetically. "What was the alternative? He knew he was dying and you told him what he wanted to hear. He had that lovely thought in his mind. You did the right thing," she said reassuringly. "Now go and wash your face and let's have a cup of tea before we start the morning routine."

I found Nurse Pendle to be very thoughtful and understanding. She might have been lazy but we managed to get through the work and still fit in lots of cups of tea.

Night duty over, it was the big night out. We were going to make a long night of it, visiting a few pubs before going to the disco. It would be the last night out for a while as we were both going on day duty and would frequently be working different shifts. I had arranged for Mary to open the fire escape so we could return whenever we wanted to.

Jumping on the bus we decided to join the older, sensible people downstairs, as there was an element of danger to Barbara climbing stairs dressed as she was. The bus, being a popular mode of transport, was full, with standing room only. It was Friday night and most people had finished their working week and were out to enjoy themselves. Huddersfield centre was very busy when we arrived. The streets were brightly lit, loud music played; the strong smell of beer, perfume and aftershave wafted under our noses as we hurried along.

Barbara didn't look a bit "out of place" as she had on the lower deck of the bus. Although I had tried to brighten myself up, I still felt rather drab in comparison. The men all looked very dapper. Fashion for men in the 1960s was not as revolutionary as it was for women but there was still a lot of change. There were a lot more options than the suit and tie. They also had choice of more colourful clothing; the patterns for men flourished, paisley, polka dots and fluorescent colours were becoming the norm. Turtlenecks with sleek lines were very commonplace, and sports shirts were frequently seen for casual wear, with the polo style being the most popular. Longer hairstyles were becoming fashionable, and it wasn't unusual to see a male with longer hair than his girlfriend.

Lord Jim's was buzzing when we arrived, already having had a few drinks on the way. It was ten o'clock as we joined the long queue outside. I was enjoying myself and it was helping to take my mind off Mr James. By three in the morning we were both intoxicated and beginning to wilt. Barbara's speech was slurred and she had difficulty walking as we fell into the taxi back to the hospital. The rain was pouring down and the ground was soggy as we staggered cross the grass towards the fire escape. It took ages, as Barbara's stiletto heels kept sinking into the mud. She was laughing and singing, and her voice was getting louder and louder. Glancing up at the building I noticed that Sister Brooks' light was on – and Barbara was on the same corridor. How was I going to get her past Sister Brooks' room?

"Ssh, Barbara. You will have to keep very quiet. Sister Brooks has her light on. Take those shoes off. We mustn't disturb her or we will be in big trouble."

My warning was useless. We managed to climb the fire escape with Barbara lagging behind me continually saying "Ssh" and giggling. Creeping past Sister Brooks' room, we could hear some movement.

"Nurses, what are you doing?" an unmistakable voice shouted. Unsurprisingly, we had been rumbled. It was difficult to remain serious as Sister Brooks appeared. She was dressed in a long, pink nylon nightdress, slippers with large bobbles on the top and rollers in her hair topped with a brown hair net!

She took us in with one look. "This is very serious and will be reported to Matron. Your parents will also need to be notified." But Barbara, in full flight, shouted back, "Tell my parents if you want. They know I stay out late."

Sister Brooks looked furious, her face turning bright red as she retorted, "Get to bed before the whole corridor is disturbed," as if it wasn't already.

I was unable to sleep. What were my parents going to think of me? Would it be instant dismissal from the course? What was I going to do? Barbara slept like a baby. She wasn't bothered in the slightest.

I never mentioned the incident to my parents, but lived in fear, expecting them to receive a letter saying that I would be expelled from the course. But Matron was not informed and our parents never received a letter. Perhaps Sister Brooks' bark was worse than her bite: the fear of what might happen, however, had been punishment enough.

# Chapter 16

I had the misfortune to work in Casualty under the strict discipline of Sister Fletcher, whom I instantly disliked and I was soon to learn that the feeling was mutual. She was probably the most miserable and least exciting person I had ever met. She was medium height, with a slim upper half and a fat bottom half. She wore a permanent scowl on her face and her wispy hair stuck out uncontrollably beneath her hat. She introduced herself with no eye contact as she looked me up and down.

"Perhaps you had better pin your hair up. It is touching your collar and looks untidy," she said, producing some hair grips from her pocket and handing them to me. How was I going to put my hair up? It was far too short. I hated her already. Almost in tears I attempted to pin it up. It looked a mess, but was the best I could do. She made no comment as I returned to the department to be shown around. In addition to the main rooms for treating very ill patients were a number of small cubicles, a plaster room and a theatre for minor operations.

"We have routine outpatient clinics weekday mornings. I will send a senior nurse to work with you this morning until she feels you are competent to assess and treat patients on your own," she explained before rushing off. Nurse Alison Gorman, a third year student, soon joined me. She had worked on the department for several weeks, but didn't appear to be enjoying it. Sister Fletcher's voice could be heard outside the cubicle shouting patients' names and directing them to the cubicles. A noisy queue was forming outside our cubicle, the seats being quickly taken. "We seem to be getting most of the work – just look at that queue, standing room only and we haven't started yet. They will be fighting over seats before long. Does she think that because there are two of us, we are going to work twice as fast?" said Alison.

"It does seem unfair as it is my first day. I hope I don't prove to be a hindrance," I replied.

"Don't worry it's not your fault. She just likes to show her authority, but I will tell her if we have too much work to cope with."

Alison didn't find time to do much teaching, but I was amazed at the speed she was able to work, quickly assessing each patient and getting on with the task in hand while remaining outwardly pleasant and calm, putting the patient at ease. We saw a wide variety of patients and were kept busy all morning, dressing wounds, removing stitches and clips, giving injections. Some patients were discharged, others were to return for further treatment. What a responsibility! It was fine while Alison was around but I couldn't imagine treating patients by myself in the clinics.

Casualty, known today as Accident and Emergency, was very different from the wards. The work was more varied and unpredictable. One minute you could be working alone in clinic, then an emergency would arrive and you found yourself in a team, saving a life.

Practice nurses were not in post until the 1970s, so Casualty got a lot of the routine work which is done in GPs' surgeries today. The majority of patients didn't complain if they had a long wait, and were grateful for their care. There was respect for the nursing and medical staff; Casualty didn't experience the abuse that A&E departments experience today.

Sister Fletcher's dislike of me became evident in my first week in Casualty. She was constantly watching what I was doing. The harder I tried, the more critical she became of my work. I was desperately unhappy and would check the roster to see if we were on duty together. I could only relax and enjoy my work when she was not around. I began to feel that I couldn't cope any longer, but complaining about senior staff could make matters more difficult.

"Are you okay? You look very pale and tired. Are you taking care of yourself?" asked Mum.

It was a much needed day off. I looked at Mum and was unable to respond. I had a lump in my throat, my eyes were stinging, and I couldn't control the tears. Mum seemed surprised at my reaction and quietly waited until I managed to compose myself.

"Sorry Mum, I can't continue with my training, I am so unhappy." I told her how Sister Fletcher was treating me and that there was nothing that I could do about it.

Mum sat deep in thought before replying. "It would be a shame to give up now after you have worked so hard. You are over half way through your training and haven't much longer to work with her. Don't let her ruin your career. Try to ignore her and just do your best. If you feel that you can't go on, that is fine, but you will need to find another job first."

Travelling back to Huddersfield on the bus, I thought about my conversation with Mum and what she had advised. She was right of course, but I felt she had been harsh saying that I had to find another job before I could leave. What would I do? I would be on my next placement before I found anything. Years later, I realised if it hadn't been for Mum, I would have handed in my resignation at that time.

Weekends were invariably busy with a variety of problems. Accidents, overdoses, attempted suicides and drunks were the norm. It was a brief encounter with each patient. They were dealt with and moved on. Why had that patient attempted suicide? When did that patient develop a drink problem and what were the circumstances leading up to it? I missed not having the opportunity of getting to know them and understanding why they had come to need our care.

One Saturday I was working a late shift, with Sister Miles in charge. She was relatively new to the hospital, but had lots of previous Casualty experience, and was very organised and efficient. She was a joy to work with.

A pretty young woman named Linda, in her early twenties, was our first emergency. Her distraught mother arrived with her. Linda was only semi-conscious, following an overdose of anti-depressants. Her mother had returned from shopping to find Linda lying on her bedroom floor. Linda had been treated for depression for several months. Although she had vomited before arriving at the hospital, she still required a stomach washout.

"Have you done a stomach washout yet, Nurse Clark?" asked Sister Miles.

"No, but I have observed a few."

"Well now is your chance. It gets easier with practice."

What a dreadful task to have to do; it was bad enough watching someone else do it. A thick rubber tube is passed down the throat and into the stomach to wash out the stomach contents. It can be an awful experience for the patient, as they often panic, gag, and sometimes attempt to pull the tube out. Linda did exceptionally well, and the procedure was soon completed. The doctor was called to put an intravenous drip up, and oxygen was administered. It felt so cruel doing the stomach washout, but the result was rewarding as Linda slowly perked up. Her mother, who had been anxiously waiting in the visitors' room, was relieved to see her daughter looking so much better. Linda was admitted to the medical ward for observation.

A much needed lull followed, with a steady stream of patients with minor problems flowing through the department: a screaming toddler who had shoved something up his nose, a lady with something in her eye, a man with a burn to his hand. I admitted a young teenager with a small laceration to his leg, which needed stitching.

"Would you like to put some stitches in, Nurse Clark? The wound should only need four at the most." Sister Miles was allowing me to gain lots of experience. Tom and his mum were happy for me to practise on him. He was a delightful boy, chatting about his hobbies and interests while I was getting my trolley ready. A small amount of local anaesthetic was injected before I started my stitching. I was surprised how easily the needle went through his young skin. Job finished, and I admired my first sewing exercise. "Well done, Nurse Clark." It was to be the only *Well done* I was likely to receive while working on Casualty. What a shame Sister Miles wasn't writing my report. Maybe she will put a good word in for me!

After a lull two policemen arrived with the first unconscious drunk of the evening (we tended to see rather a lot of the police during the weekend; not surprisingly, nurses and policemen frequently dated). We needed to observe such patients to ensure there wasn't an underlying problem such as diabetes. Drunks that were just causing a nuisance were taken to the police cells to sleep it off.

Next came ambulances with victims of a road traffic accident. Two young men had hit a wall on a bend on a busy road; fortunately no other vehicles were involved. Both men had multiple fractures. The passenger was unconscious, having also sustained a severe head injury, which was frequently seen in car accident victims. I found it deeply upsetting as my thoughts went back to ward 1 and the awful trauma that Michael and other road traffic victims had to endure. Unlike in modern cars today, car drivers and passengers in the 1960s didn't have the protection of seat belts and air bags. It was not until 1983 that the use of seat belts in the front of cars became compulsory, and 1991 before it was compulsory for adults to belt up in the back seats too.

Thankfully I was asked to leave the accident scene and go to the plaster room, which I thoroughly enjoyed – it was so messy and reminded me of being a child. Archie was five, a cheeky little chap. He had a thick mop of unruly blond hair, his mischievous blue eyes shone through his thick rimmed spectacles, and he had the most wonderful smile exposing huge dimples in his cheeks.

He had fractured his arm playing football in the garden with his dad. It was almost 10pm, was I ever going to get off duty? I knew that I hadn't been mistaken for night staff, as the staff on my shift were still around. Unfortunately we didn't get paid for overtime. Archie had a puzzled expression as he glanced at my apron and white wellington boots that were far too big.

"Hello Archie. I am Nurse Clark. I have come to put a special bandage on your arm to make it better."

"You look funny," he giggled. "Why are you wearing wellies, does it rain in the hospital?

"No, it doesn't rain but it gets very wet in this room: just watch what happens. Right young man, let us make this arm better then you can go home to bed. You must be very tired like me. We need to put something nice and soft on your arm first to keep it warm," I explained as I put a stockinette sleeve over his fractured arm. Archie gave his concerned dad a big smile. He watched with interest as I wet a roll of plaster of Paris bandage and, dripping white fluid over my apron and wellies, I applied the wet bandage over the stockinette sleeve, smoothed it out and brought over the edges of the stockinette to make a cuff.

"Look how wet this room is now. Aren't I messy? I need to make sure it is not too tight. Your fingers look nice and pink, can you wiggle them? The sleeve will go hard and your dad will be able to do a drawing on it for you. I will go and get Sister to check that I have done a good job before you go."

Archie had cheered me up at the end of a very long day. Dead on my feet, I was allowed to go off duty. It was 11pm and I was on an early shift the following morning.

At the end of my placement I received my report from Sister Fletcher. As expected, it wasn't good. She was aware of my disappointment, and that I didn't agree with all she had written, but as students we were not allowed to question and I reluctantly signed it. Fortunately students today have a voice, being encouraged to question and disagree if necessary.

How times have changed since the introduction of Advanced Care Paramedics in 1984. Medical care can now be provided at an advanced life support level in the pre-hospital environment, in medical emergencies and trauma.

Recently I had to be admitted to our local A&E. The emergency response paramedic arrived promptly. He assessed my condition and provided care and treatment, which continued on the way to the hospital. The department was extremely busy. It brought back lots of memories as I watched nurses and medical staff rushing about trying to get patients treated as quickly as possible.

Today the equipment is much more sophisticated and efficient and, with advance in technology, more refined and less invasive investigations and treatments are available. Patients are more likely to survive heart attacks, strokes and serious accidents and make a better recovery.

# Chapter 17

The sky was a cold grey and the trees were swaying in the sharp breeze. Their leaves were edged with orange-brown. Can autumn really be coming? Time is going so quickly, I am half way through my training already and have so much to learn before qualifying. I am working back on the female medical ward for a week, due to staff shortages.

I made a terrible mistake on my first day on the ward. Everyone was highly stressed, rushing about to ensure patients were getting their lunch.

Sister Bell hurriedly greeted me. She was more intimidating than I had remembered. Her general appearance did not help matters. She looked unkempt, her dishevelled, greasy hair was in desperate need of a wash, and her uniform was hanging loosely on her thin frame. She looked ill.

"I am unable to give the report at present, Nurse Clark. As you can see, we are extremely busy. Hopefully things will settle down before long. Could you give an injection of Largactil to Mrs Bailey before helping with the lunchtime routine?" I followed her into the treatment room where she handed me the patient's treatment sheet, and the ampoule of Largactil. After checking the dose was correct, she left me to prepare the injection and give it to the patient. I caught Staff Nurse as she passed the treatment room, to ask her where I would find Mrs Bailey. She glanced at the treatment sheet.

"Mrs Bailey is down the corridor in the main ward, first patient on the left," she said before rushing away. The directions were correct. Mrs Bailey was an elderly lady who I imagined as stunningly beautiful in her youth. She wore her silver hair short and neatly waved, her face was highlighted with powder with a thin application of pink lipstick. She wore a pink, floral nightdress, obviously a lady who cared about her appearance.

"Is it Mrs Bailey?" I inquired.

"Yes love, but do call me Enid. Everyone else does and it makes me feel younger."

"I am Nurse Clark. I have just started on the ward, and Sister has asked me to give you an injection."

"Yes, that's fine, love."

I pulled the screens around the bed and checked Mrs Bailey's details. The name on her arm band and her treatment sheets at the bottom of her bed agreed she was Enid Bailey. Looking at her treatment sheet, she didn't appear to have had a Largactil injection while she had been in hospital. Largactil was a tranquilliser and sedative. Enid already seemed very relaxed, but I didn't feel the need to question it: Sister had asked me to give it, Staff Nurse had directed me to the patient and it was written up on the treatment sheet. I didn't know Enid's medical history – maybe the drug was given for other conditions. Enid was happy to receive her injection, and common with the majority of patients at that time, she didn't query it. Nowadays people are more questioning and a great number of people who require nursing care are those who have long- term conditions and know much more about their care than they might have years ago. Enid thanked me and I left her to carry on with my work.

A good while later, with the ward still in chaos, and still having not received a ward report, I answered a call from one of the side wards. I was confronted by a very angry, agitated lady, a pronounced vertical furrow between her thick brows that deepened as she glared at me. "Where is my injection? Sister said that I would be given it ages ago. How much longer do I have to wait?" she shouted.

"I am so sorry, but the ward is exceptionally busy at the moment. I will go and find out for you. What name is it?"

"Mrs Bailey," she angrily replied.

I was barely able to speak as I read the name on the treatment sheet – *Mrs Enid Bailey*. There were two patients on the ward with exactly the same Christian and surname! I had given the injection to the wrong Mrs Bailey. What was I going to do? Whose fault was it? It was a catalogue of errors. Should Sister and Staff Nurse have informed me that there were two patients with the same name? Had Staff Nurse forgotten as she directed me to the patient? Should Sister have observed me giving the injection, particularly as I didn't know any of the patients? Ultimately it was my fault; I had checked the patient's name, but had failed to check her date of birth. Hopefully this type of mistake does not happen today, as student nurses work closely with their mentors.

Sister Bell was understanding as I explained what I had done. It had to be reported to the senior nursing and medical staff, plus the first Mrs Bailey, who'd had a very relaxing sleep, and had not suffered any ill effects from the drug. The second Mrs Bailey eventually received her much needed injection which worked a treat. She spent the rest of the day totally relaxed. I had learned my lesson and never made the same mistake again. It made me aware how easily mistakes could be made.

My working week didn't improve much, though fortunately Edith had been discharged, so I didn't have to play the role of Denise to encourage her to eat instead of throwing food at me. Sadly we had several deaths on the ward, one being a young lady in her early twenties. Janet was attractive and intelligent with a bubbly personality. Her boyfriend clearly adored her. She had her whole life in front of her but had suffered from asthma since early childhood, and had been admitted to hospital having an acute asthma attack. Her condition was gradually improving when she suddenly became very breathless, and despite attempts by the medical staff to stabilise her, she died. It was such a shock to all the staff. Her family and boyfriend were devastated: their world had been shattered.

Fortunately death from asthma is uncommon, but in the 1960s, a short lived epidemic of deaths caused by asthma occurred, which some thought might be the result of a toxic effect of one of the asthma inhalers at the time. This has been disputed over the years and other factors may have been of importance. It is unlikely that we shall ever know the complete story surrounding that event.

Most asthma deaths are caused by under-treatment of patients, and it has been shown that two-thirds of asthma deaths would have been prevented with adequate treatment. I was relieved when the week was over.

Barbara was still on my corridor but I hadn't seen her for ages, as we had been working opposite shifts. Desperately in need of cheering up, I decided to see if she was around. I was in luck; the door opened as a smiling face greeted me.

"Hi stranger. How are you?" I asked.

"I'm fine. It's lovely to see you. Come in and let's have a catch up," she replied.

"I've had a dreadful week, Barbara, and need someone to talk to."

"Sit down if you can find a space and I will make us a drink, and we can stuff ourselves with cake and biscuits. That should make you feel much better. Do you want tea or something stronger? I have got some wine if you prefer." Barbara never disappointed. We ate, drank wine and talked for the following two hours. Barbara had the knack of making things seem much brighter. We arranged to have a much overdue night out and I left feeling tired, dizzy and bloated after all the indiscriminate snacking.

# Chapter 18

Nurse Crowther was a clumsy individual. She was a large lady, with a lived-in face which held minimal expression, making her look considerably older than her mid-thirties. Her posture was dreadful. She walked with her back arched, head down, glancing at the ground, her large glasses perched on the end of her nose. The top half of her body, possibly due to the weight of her large bosom, would arrive before her bottom half.

We worked on the male surgical ward together, where I witnessed her bumbling around, terrifying patients and causing havoc. Why had she chosen nursing as a career? She was considerably older than the majority of students. An intelligent lady, she was a history graduate who had decided on a career change. She was my senior, nearing the end of her third year. How had she managed to get so far? It was definitely not due to her practical skills; she appeared inept as a nurse.

Surgery is of no great interest to me and I was unable to raise much enthusiasm working on the ward, but must work hard to avoid getting another bad report. Fortunately the Senior Sister is more human than Sister Fletcher.

Two weeks into my placement, Sister Rhodes, the Nurse Tutor whom I had managed to avoid for ages, was coming to assess my dressing technique. Fortunately my patient was a young man who'd had an emergency appendicectomy five days previously. I had been working on the ward when John was admitted in severe pain, and I had got to know him reasonably well. Although it's a relatively minor operation today, in the sixties patients spent seven to ten days in hospital following an appendicectomy. John was quite excited about the tutor coming to assess me, promising that he would behave himself and be the model patient. I checked my appearance before Sister Rhodes arrived; hat on straight, hair not touching collar, dress and apron clean, I think she will approve. I wait nervously in the treatment room. Sister Rhodes arrives promptly.

"Good morning, Nurse Clark," she said. "How are you enjoying working on a general surgical ward?"

"I am finding it very enjoyable," I lied. "It is so interesting and the work is very varied."

"Oh that's good to hear. You should be able to put a lot of theory into practice, which is always very helpful. I need to see you setting a dressing trolley, and changing a wound dressing. I gather Sister has organised a patient for you."

"Yes Sister. John is five days post-op following an appendicectomy. His wound has been healing well, so I am going to put suture removing equipment on the trolley in case his stitches are ready for removal." Forward planning should get me some Brownie points, I thought. I continued to prepare my trolley carefully, hoping to impress her further.

The task was much easier than in the Old Infirmary as we now had a Central Sterilising Department responsible for sterilising all equipment in the hospital. The department not only sterilised syringes and dressings but produced special dressing packs containing towels, swabs and instruments for most kinds of dressings.

After cleaning my trolley, I put a sterile dressing pack and suture removing pack on the top shelf where all the sterile equipment is kept. How easy is that? It should contain all that I require to do the dressing – much easier and quicker than having to remember all the equipment you will need and sterilise it on the spot. I place an unsterile receiver for dirty swabs and dressings, plus antiseptic solutions, on the bottom shelf.

I introduce John to Sister Rhodes and leave them chatting as I pull the curtains around the bed, put on my gown and mask, wash my hands and put on sterile gloves. Although the trolley has virtually set itself, there is still lots to remember. I remove the dirty dressing with a pair of forceps and place it in the unsterile bowl. Although Sister Rhodes is talking to John, I am fully aware that she is watching my every move.

The wound looks clean and is almost healed.

"What are you going to do with the stitches, Nurse? Do you think they are ready for removal?" she asked.

"It is not fully healed; the edges are slightly inflamed, so I was considering taking alternate stitches out," I replied.

"I agree, Nurse. Some do look ready to be removed."

I carefully cleaned the wound, remembering the technique I had been taught. Clean the wound from top to bottom and from within out, only using each swab once and not wiping it up and down the wound. You must use sterile forceps to pick up the swabs, not your fingers, which would be an easier option. John's alternate stitches were easily removed, a technique that I had mastered quite well, and I put a clean dressing in place.

"That feels wonderful, Nurse Clark. Thanks a lot," said John. "My wound was beginning to feel tight and had become quite itchy, hopefully it will now settle down a bit."

"That is a good sign; it must be healing. I am sure the remainder of your stitches will be ready to be removed in two days," I replied.

Sister Rhodes was satisfied with my removal of sutures and wound dressing technique and signed me off as competent in the procedures.

Although Sister Farmer, the Senior Sister, was a dedicated nurse and excellent teacher, who made work more interesting, I knew I didn't want to work in surgical nursing. I felt it rewarding observing how quickly most of the patients recovered following surgery, when the offending bit that was causing problems had been removed. It could however be very upsetting to see patients who could not be cured.

Peter was one of those patients, a young man in his late thirties who had an inoperable tumour. He would writhe about in agony, screaming with the severe pain. All we could do was administer pain relief. When the morphine numbed his pain, he relaxed his grip on the sheet and opened his eyes. He was so grateful; it was dreadfully upsetting.

I wasn't enjoying the general routine on the ward. Pre-operative care included passing nasogastric tubes, inserting catheters, and giving enemas. Post-surgery came changing drips, giving injections, wound dressings, suture and clip removal. Some of the wounds were quite repulsive and foul smelling. It was all about making patients comfortable and mobilising them as soon as possible.

"Nurse Clark," shouted Sister Farmer. "Could I have a word with you in my office?" My first thought: *What have I done wrong?*

"Close the door Nurse and sit down."

It must be something very serious if she is asking me to sit down.

"I need to ask a big favour of you. I should have been off duty at 5pm and am unable to stay any longer. All the routine work is up to date but I am reluctant to leave Nurse Crowther in charge. Although she is very knowledgeable, her practical skills leave a lot to be desired. Could you please keep a discreet eye on her? Sister Arnott from female orthopaedics has agreed to pop on the ward frequently to check things are running smoothly, but please notify her if you are at all concerned. I am sorry to put this responsibility on you, but the other two nurses are very junior. There shouldn't be any major problems."

"Yes Sister," I reluctantly replied. It was a big ask. Did she really think that I was capable of keeping an eye on such a clumsy nurse? It was already 6pm, so only three hours left, if we were to get off duty in time. It was to be the longest three hours I had ever worked. Not only was Nurse Crowther clumsy, she was extremely noisy. She was heard long before she became visible, shouting and clumping around.

Her inability to run the ward efficiently soon became evident. She rushed around like a mad woman becoming more and more dishevelled, well out of her depth. She enjoyed showing her authority: *Change that drip, help that patient to the toilet, give this injection* she could be heard shouting, while clattering around bumping into things. Watching her change Mr Holt's blood drip was the highlight of the evening, blood spurting everywhere.

"Nurse Clark, change this bed while I go and change my apron," she demanded, angrily rushing off to the cloakroom. She was so abrupt that I felt like hitting her. "Take no notice of her, Nurse. She's a nasty piece of work. Just keep her away from me," said Mr Holt.

"Where do I start? I think it will be easier to get you cleaned up first and sat in a chair, and then I will deal with your bed," I was thinking out aloud. We looked at each other then started to laugh uncontrollably. Life certainly wasn't dull when Nurse Crowther was around.

Sister Arnott checked frequently to see that we were all bearing up and rising to the challenge. It was after ten when we managed to get off duty. It had certainly been a learning curve, and an experience I didn't wish to repeat.

Nurse Crowther failed her State Final Examination, and as far as we knew she transferred to another hospital to re-sit the exam. We never heard from her again; she may have continued to terrorise patients for many years.

Joining the smoking brigade had not come easy. My first cigarette, given to me by a nursing colleague, caused a fit of coughing following the first drag, and left a foul taste in my mouth. How could anyone enjoy the experience? I did, however, manage to perfect the art, following lots of practice. It soon became a very costly habit, but had a calming effect, helping me to cope with the stresses of the job. Smoking Consulate menthol cigarettes, I fooled myself that they were less harmful than other cigarettes. The habit only lasted several years, but during that time I met lots of new nursing friends. Most of the smokers were senior nurses, which enabled us to have our meals at the same table in the dining room before progressing to our corner of the lounge, to the disapproval of the non-smokers. Mum and Dad never knew that I smoked until years later, but must have been curious to know why I had the need to borrow so much more money.

## Chapter 19

A much awaited Christmas had arrived and I was fortunate to have been given Christmas Day off this year.

Dad loved Christmas. He would make a big effort to ensure it a very special occasion for all the family. Many years later, following his death, I learnt that Dad had married his first wife on Christmas Eve. She died fourteen months later, leaving him with a two month old daughter to care for. It must have been a time of mixed emotions for him, which he never made obvious. He never spoke about it.

Christmas was spent in the front room, with Dad in charge of the decorations. The large artificial Christmas tree would be taken out of its box and placed in the corner of the room, decorated with baubles and lights with a fairy stuck on the top. The lights always caused problems; Dad would invariably have to patiently fiddle about with them for ages to get them to light up. Colourful paper decorations were pinned across the ceiling with a large paper bell hanging down in the centre. It all looked very colourful.

It had now become a real treat to eat at home. Although money was often short, we were always well fed; meat or fish, potatoes and three vegetables for dinner, with a pudding to finish off. I particularly enjoyed Mum's home-made rice pudding. It took hours to cook but the smell of nutmeg during cooking was divine. The finished article had a thick brown skin on top which was very tasty. It was all such a contrast to the hospital food which was often very stodgy and the way it was dolloped on your plate made it look most unappetising. The strong cabbage smell that wafted around the dining room didn't help, but we always ate the food without complaint because we were so hungry.

Mum and Dad would prepare and cook the Christmas dinner together, with help from me and my sister if needed. Jane was now fourteen years old, so I no longer had to pretend about Santa Claus. It was an early rise on that bitterly cold and frosty Christmas morning. I was so excited to be at home. We dressed quickly in the freezing bedroom and crept downstairs to view the presents beneath the tree. We were surprised to be greeted by roaring fires in both rooms, it felt warm and inviting. The turkey was already in the oven and Mum and Dad were in the kitchen chopping vegetables.

It was customary on Christmas morning to have breakfast then gather round the tree for the opening of presents. It must have been a struggle financially for my parents to give us the presents we wanted, but they always did. We also received presents from relatives and neighbours. Dad was relieved that the tree lights were working. As usual presents were stacked high beneath. It took ages as we slowly opened each present, not wanting the experience to end.

It continued to be a busy day with lots of laughter. At dinner there were the four of us. The table was set in the front room, with the best table cloth, crockery and cutlery; it looked very posh. Dad proudly carved the large turkey, which we ate with all the trimmings, potatoes and a selection of fresh vegetables, followed by a large helping of Christmas pudding.

There was hardly time to wash up, and for the meal to be digested, before the table was re-set for tea – a buffet of cold meats, pork pie and salad, plus trifle, cake and mince pies. It was such a busy day, with relatives, friends and neighbours popping in. Most of them I hadn't seen for such a long time; we had so much catching up to do. Although I now had less in common with the people back home, my roots would always be there, and I thoroughly enjoyed the gathering. I retired to bed late that night feeling relaxed, contented and very full.

It was an early rise on Boxing Day as I had to reluctantly return to the hospital for a late shift. As there was no bus service, I had to rely on Dad to take me back.

The year before, I had taken driving lessons on my days off which had not been an enjoyable experience. My instructor was a large gentleman with a voice to match. He taught in a Ford Cortina, which was a big car at the time, so I had to sit on a large cushion to see out of the windscreen. He was very strict and had strange methods of teaching, like pressing a plank of wood on your foot to teach clutch control. It seemed to have worked as I had passed my driving test, but would not be able to afford a car of my own for a few years unless my income increased dramatically.

# Chapter 20

It was the first day of our second study block and everyone looked extremely tired and unenthusiastic; even Ann was not her usual chatty self. We were all running out of steam. Surprisingly, Linda was still on the course, which was quite an achievement as she was becoming increasingly unhappy, but desperately wanted to make her father, who was a strong disciplinarian, proud of her achievements.

"Come on you lot, why do you all look so miserable? We have only a year left to do, it will fly past," said Mary, as she cheerily entered the room, sat down and noisily emptied a pile of books on her desk. What a transformation! She had become so confident. "You look keen Mary," I said to her. "I have been told we have lots to learn in this study block and that the exams at the end are really difficult. I am not looking forward to it."

"We will get through it. We are all in the same boat and can help each other. It certainly beats working those long shifts in hospital," she replied.

Although the Irish girls often tended to socialise with their own circle, the entire group continued to get along very well. We were all young and like-minded, understanding what each other was going through. We'd had to mature quickly, but were still able to revert back to carefree mode and enjoy ourselves.

We were all feeling uplifted, thanks to Mary, by the time Miss Hillman arrived. Her appearance was as immaculate as ever, even down to her highly polished shoes. The morning was spent discussing the study block and what was expected of us. Sister Rhodes and Sister Kershaw would do the practical teaching, but lectures would be given by the Consultants in their own field. At the end of the block they would set the examination papers and mark them. Lectures were to be given in medicine, surgery, ENT, ophthalmology, orthopaedics, gynaecology and paediatrics. Everyone was getting anxious just thinking about it.

"Don't worry Nurses, I know it all sounds very daunting, but you will be surprised how much you already know," said Miss Hillman.

*Or we might be surprised how little we know* whispered Ann.

It didn't take us long to adapt to the classroom setting, but it still felt strange having to wear our uncomfortable uniform. I am sure we would have been able to concentrate more if we had been allowed to dress in mufti. Miss Hillman was soon to be proved right; surprisingly we did have quite a lot of knowledge. Most of the lecturers were able to make their subjects interesting and hold our concentration. Mr Bartley, the gynaecology Consultant, was the exception. He was a slim, middle aged man of medium height, always smartly dressed in an immaculate suit, waistcoat and tie. Unfortunately, his lectures were boring. He would enter the room in his authoritative manner, glare at us all, and then constantly pace across the room staring at the wall in front of him, speaking in a monotonous voice. It didn't help that his lectures were mostly after lunch when the carbs had kicked in.

On one occasion I was feeling very sleepy and had completely lost interest. Listening to his voice droning on, I decided to rest my eyes for a while. All that I could hear were odd words like hysterectomy, myomectomy, salpingo-oophorectomy, colporrhaphy. Was he speaking some foreign language? I hadn't done my gynaecology placement and had no idea what he was talking about. How was I supposed to remember all these words and be able to spell them?

Feeling confident he wouldn't notice me sitting at the front of the classroom and believing lecturers always looked to the back of the room, I started to drift off to sleep. I was soon startled by Mr Bartley as he shouted, "Nurse, you have obviously no interest in being here, so gather your belongings and leave the room. In future only attend my lectures if you are going to pay attention." Red faced and extremely embarrassed, I picked up my books and departed.

I did attend the rest of Mr Bartley's lectures, tried to look interested and, somehow, managed to keep awake. The other subject which many of us struggled with was ophthalmology, but fortunately, Mr Swinton made his lectures interesting. He had a chubby red face, with the most infectious smile. He was passionate about his subject and delivered his lectures in a witty manner which held our concentration.

Mr Harris was the senior physician, a strange little man with a rugged face and pointed features. Like Mr Bartley, he was always impeccably dressed. His black hair was smoothed neatly in place with Brylcreem; a bushy moustache completed the image. He was very brusque and frightened junior and senior staff alike. I had met him several times on the ward and didn't intend falling asleep in his lectures! Medicine continued to interest me and I learnt a lot from his sessions.

We all behaved ourselves while he was around. The room went quiet the minute he entered the room and remained so until he left.

Mr Illingworth, the ENT Consultant, was my favourite. A tall, slim man with a gentle personality, he wasn't bumptious like most of the other surgeons I had come across. He was very approachable and staff and patients respected him. I had observed his work on the ward where he spoke reassuringly to his patients, making them feel relaxed. His personality filtered through to the classroom, ensuring his lectures were delivered in a relaxed manner, allowing us plenty of time to ask questions.

By the end of the block we were all exhausted and stressed at the thought of the impending exams. It had been extremely hard: work, bed and work some more, with no respite. I had done hours of studying but was unable to clearly remember everything. I had bought myself a gynaecology book and had read every page of it, hoping to retain enough to pass the exam. Fortunately our exam papers have a number and not a name so Mr Bartley won't know when he is marking mine.

On our day off before the start of the exams, Mary, Ann and I decided to do some last minute revision, which was a big mistake. We became increasingly anxious and thoroughly confused. By early evening we had all retired to our own rooms. It was a beautiful spring evening: how I wished I was out with my friends enjoying myself. I lay on top of the bed and must have dozed off because it was dark when I woke up. I was hungry and thirsty. I slowly uncurled my limbs and stretched my spine. Following a relaxing bath and something to eat and drink, I retired to bed for a restless night's sleep.

Each exam was two hours long, and consisting of four questions to be answered in essay form; no choices of questions were given and spelling was taken into account. We all found them difficult and welcomed the week's holiday that followed which I spent relaxing and sleeping.

Two blue stripes on my hat! I was now proud to be a third year student nurse. I had passed all my examinations with good grades. The biggest surprise was the results of my gynaecology and ophthalmology exams; I had the highest pass mark in the group. Sadly, not everyone had passed all the exams so emotions were very mixed. I was now ready to start the last year of my training with my theatre placement. Bridget, an Irish girl in our group, would also be in theatre so at least there would be one familiar face. Although the Irish girls tended to be very clannish, I felt that I knew Bridget quite well. She was a most likeable character, friendly and cheerful with a wicked sense of humour. She was frequently in trouble but it didn't seem to bother her.

We stuck close together as we entered the large theatre doors at 7. 20am, arriving early to make a good impression. A long corridor lay ahead of us. We stood to attention quietly waiting to be met by the Theatre Superintendent. Sister Stanton's rapid footsteps were soon heard coming towards us. She was a middle aged spinster who had worked in theatre since qualifying and apparently knew everything that went on. She had a reputation of disliking students and would humiliate them at every opportunity. We were both visibly shaking. Bridget nudged me and whispered, "Don't think we should mess about when she's around."

Sister Stanton introduced herself, and then as she quickly turned on her heels, abruptly ordered us to follow her. It was difficult to keep up with her as she rushed down the corridor, her head bobbing from side to side.

We soon found ourselves in the changing rooms; everywhere looked very posh in comparison to the Old Infirmary, very spacious and modern. After showing us around, Sister Stanton instructed us to change into our theatre uniform. She would return shortly.

Bridget was soon in fits of laughter. "Just look at the state of me; is it possible to find a dress to fit? This is the fourth one I've tried, it says small on the label but it is huge. I will trip up if I try to walk."

I turned to look at Bridget and started to laugh until the tears rolled down my cheeks. The dress hung on her small frame and wrapped around her ankles. She was such a tonic.

I sympathised. "I spent a few hours in theatre in the Old Infirmary and had the same problem. All the dresses were far too big but we did have a belt with them so could at least hitch them up a bit. I look just as ridiculous. Let's see if we can find some that are smaller." After further searching we were in luck.

"This is a slight improvement but it will still take a while for me to grow into it. I never thought I would appreciate my starched uniform," Bridget remarked.

We looked so alike in our theatre uniforms; we were the same stature, both had brown eyes and short dark hair. With caps and masks on, it would be difficult to tell the difference. Fortunately we had different accents!

We place our belongings in our allocated lockers and wait for the return of the dragon. Sister Stanton soon rushes in, and not commenting on our appearance takes us on a tour of the theatres. There is so much to take in: how were we expected to remember everything? Our first morning is mainly spent learning the names of the instruments so we know which to hand the surgeon. What a scary thought! It is something I am dreading as most surgeons are said to be very short tempered.

Bridget and I work together all day, reciting the names of the instruments as we do the mundane jobs. Sister Stanton will check that we have learnt them all at the end of our shift. The monotony is broken in the afternoon; we are allowed to follow a patient from the anaesthetic room, observe the operation, and then hand over to the Ward Nurse in the recovery room.

Ian was in his early twenties and had been admitted the previous day for an appendicectomy. The Ward Nurse accompanied him to the anaesthetic room where she was relieved by the Theatre Staff Nurse. She passed over Ian's records, treatment sheets and X-rays before leaving him in our care. Ian was very relaxed following his pre-medication injection, a sedative combined with a drug to prevent excessive secretions and relax his muscles, which had been given on the ward an hour previously. The anaesthetist, a kindly young man, reassured Ian before anaesthetising him. It fascinated me how instantly he became unconscious. *What a responsibility the anaesthetist has* I thought to myself. *He sits quietly at the head of the operating table, administering drugs and closely observing the patient without much recognition.*

"I feel quite anxious about watching this operation," Bridget said, as we stood close to each other waiting for the surgeon to arrive. "I didn't think we would observe any surgery so soon in our placement."

"I feel the same. I have observed an operation before but it was only the removal of a lipoma. Just remember not to touch anything, remain upright and try not to vomit," I replied.

I glanced at Ian's limp, unconscious body and wondered if surgeons thought of them as living patients when they operated. Surely they have to fully detach themselves from the person as they cut into their flesh. No wonder they become short tempered under all the stress.

Although a third year student, I felt inexperienced as I observed the staff efficiently working together as a team. The atmosphere was surprisingly tranquil and listening to the *whoosh. . . . . . whoosh* of the anaesthetic machine, I soon began to feel quite relaxed. The operation went very quickly with no problems; incision made, appendix removed, sutures and dressing in place. Bridget and I hadn't managed to see much but at least we were still standing.

In the post-operative room Staff Nurse watched Ian closely until he regained consciousness and he was soon collected and taken back to the ward. We were both relieved when our first shift was over and that we had managed to memorise the main instruments.

In addition to spending our first few days cleaning, changing washbowls and learning names of instruments we had to learn how to be a runner, which is the primary role of the student nurse. Gauze swabs, instruments and needles are counted before they are used and again prior to the wound being sewn up, to ensure that nothing is left inside the patient. A mobile rack containing pegs is used to hang the dirty swabs, often dripping pools of blood over the floor.

"Are you enjoying theatre?" asked Bridget, as we walked to the dining room for lunch.

"Not really. I feel like a cleaner, not what I expected to be doing in my third year," I replied.

"No, me neither, but the theatre staff are a good team and very helpful. It's nice to have our coffee breaks in the theatre sitting room with them, makes you feel you are part of the team at least."

"Yes it helps to get to know them as you don't get much opportunity to have a chat while you're working. It's a shame we have to go to the dining room for our main meals. It takes so long to walk there and back; we don't have much time to eat our food. No wonder I have indigestion."

"Oh, I forgot to tell you," said Bridget, grinning. "I got told off by Sister Stanton the other day. She called me Nurse Clark, so must have thought I was you. It wasn't anything serious so I didn't make her any the wiser. Hope you don't mind."

"I will forgive you this once, but don't make a habit of it," I replied as we both started laughing. Several weeks into my placement Sister Stanton informs me that I will be taking my first case. She will scrub up as well and guide me through it. It is a hysterectomy. Fortunately Mr Laycock is the surgeon as Mr Bartley is on annual leave. As I carefully scrub my hands and forearms under Sister Stanton's watchful eye, I remember my first time in theatre watching the surgeon scrub up and thinking that one day I would have to learn the procedure. Here I was at last ready to take my first case; this is more fitting for a third year student nurse.

After rinsing my hands and drying them on a sterile towel, I pick up my sterile gown, and insert my arms into the long sleeves, holding the ties out so they can be tied behind me. The gown is so long it is almost sweeping the floor; I am afraid I might trip over it and fall flat on my face. I put on my rubber gloves and walk slowly to the table of instruments, remembering to hold my hands up. Sister Stanton is soon by my side and I begin to feel more relaxed. Mr Laycock arrives promptly; he seems to be quite a jolly chap.

"Good morning, Sister, lovely to see you. I gather Mrs Baker is first on the list for a hysterectomy."

"That is correct Mr Laycock. This is Nurse Clark, she is a third year student and this is her first case, so I will be guiding her through the operation."

"That is fine Sister," replied Mr Laycock as he glanced at me. "I am sure she will cope well with you instructing her."

I look at Mrs Baker's unconscious body lying on the operating table. She is an overweight lady in her late forties. She has had five children which is reflected in the appearance of her flabby belly, covered in stretch marks. The atmosphere was very calm as Mr Laycock gently swabbed the abdomen with iodine, placed sterile sheets around the area and fixed them with towel clips. He quickly makes a neat incision with his delicate hands. I feel as if I am having a dream as I hand Mr Laycock the instruments.

Sister Stanton is most helpful, preventing me from making mistakes. I find it difficult to comprehend that this is a living person as I peer into the abdomen. I watch with interest as the uterus is removed; it doesn't look at all like the diagram in my anatomy book. The wound is neatly sewn up and I sigh with relief as I place a sterile dressing over the wound.

Before leaving theatre, I also watch Mr Illingworth perform a stapedectomy. In the 1960s, stapes surgery reached its heyday with experienced surgeons doing high volumes of this operation. A binocular operating microscope was used for high magnification of the very small structures in the middle ear.

I was intrigued as I watched the delicate operation through the ear canal, replacing the stapes with a prosthetic artificial stapes using specialised microsurgical instruments. My thoughts went back to Bill and how the operation had transformed his life. How rewarding surgery can be.

I had found theatre interesting, but, like Bridget, I had missed the patient contact and knew it was not where I wanted to work.

# Chapter 21

The midday sunshine streamed through my bedroom window as I attempted to put my blackout in place ready for my third year night duty. It was the summer of 1968, the weather was hot and the corridor outside my room was noisy with a group of new intake students. One of the students had moved next door to me. She seemed very popular with her colleagues, who would frequently congregate in her room to socialise and play loud music.

How was I going to rest? I had already complained about the noise on several occasions. Sister Brooks had better not complain about my blackout, I thought: if this noise continues, she will have to find me a dark quiet room somewhere. My placement is on the gynaecology ward, and nearing the end of my training I will be in charge, so will need to remain very alert. What a frightening thought.

Relief came when the students left for their afternoon study; I curled up in bed, ear plugs in place, and slowly drifted into a light sleep.

I was abruptly woken by a loud thumping on my door. I was furious as I slowly rolled out of bed and groggily made my way to the door. I was ready for Sister Brooks; it hadn't taken her long to notice my blackout. I flung the door open only to be confronted with Barbara's smiling face.

"Oh, were you asleep? I'm so sorry," said Barbara apologetically. "I forgot you were starting night duty."

"Don't worry. I thought it was our friend Sister Brooks, about to complain about my blackout again. I was ready to give her a mouthful. What time is it?" I asked, taking my earplugs out. "These things aren't much good if a knock at the door wakens me."

Barbara laughed. "You do look a bit rough, but I did knock loudly a few times before you answered. It's just gone twenty past four, plenty of time for you to look gorgeous by the time you reach the ward. Just thought I'd pop in for a quick catch-up as we haven't seen each other for a while. Shall I make a cup of tea?"

"Please, that should help to kick start me." I removed the blackout and drew the curtains back while Barbara was preparing the tea. What a glorious summer day. I opened the window to the smell of newly mown grass and the sound of the leaves gently rustling in the warm breeze. How I would enjoy spending the evening with Barbara, relaxing in the sunshine, drinking and laughing. Instead I had seven nights' hard work in front of me. I thought it would become easier the more senior I became, but I am finding the work more stressful with all the added responsibility. Only eight months left to the final examinations; I keep telling myself it will all be worth it.

Barbara arrived back with a tray of tea, cake and biscuits. I soon begin to feel more awake. Barbara is her usual happy self but there is something about her that concerns me. She looks rather pale and appears to have lost weight.

"Are you okay Barbara?" I enquire. "You look a bit pasty."

"Yes, fine thanks. Had a bit of a cold and sore throat but now feeling tons better. Look at the time, it's after six, I'll get off and let you get organised. I've got a pile of washing to do;

not many clean clothes left. Good luck for tonight, I hope the ward is quiet."

Eager to leave, she quickly gave me a big hug, grabbed the tray and hesitantly turned around as she reached the door.

"Can I ask you a big favour?" She said, "I have a doctor's appointment tomorrow at five-thirty and wondered if you would be able to come with me. I know you will be tired being on nights, but I could do with a bit of support."

"Yes, of course I can, give me a knock around four-ish to make sure I'm awake. What on earth is wrong?" Barbara was holding back the tears as she swallowed hard. "I have missed two periods and am late again. I am worried as I have started to feel very lethargic and sickly."

I had never seen her look so upset. Putting my arm around her shoulders I replied, "Don't worry, it could be due to the stress of nursing. I missed two periods at the start of training but am fine now. Try to have a good night's sleep and I will see you tomorrow."

As I opened the door and watched her leave, I desperately hoped that her fears were wrong.

# Chapter 22

Barbara is uppermost in my thoughts as I cross to the hospital. The stress of my impending night duty now seems insignificant. It is a beautiful summer evening. I close my eyes momentarily, feeling the softness of the warm breeze on my face. The smell of the grass had now been overwhelmed by the smell of cabbage wafting over from the kitchen.

The coffee lounge, as usual, resembled a pub, full of noise, laughter and smoke. Bridget's voice could be heard way above the rest. She was sitting in the corner of the room with Mary. Fortunately they were also on night duty, which should help to keep my spirits up during the next three months. After a coffee and much needed cigarettes to steady our nerves, we walked to our respective wards, sucking extra strong mints in an attempt to conceal our smoky breath.

I felt envious that Bridget and Mary were working on male wards. I found it more difficult nursing females and often wondered why they seemed more demanding. Many of the patients were older than me, married with families. How could a young, single girl comprehend the difficult lives some of them led?

Up to that time many married women would leave their jobs to look after their homes; their husbands were expected to keep them. It was not unusual in many jobs for married women not to be employed. The radical political movements of the sixties blew apart this repressive and stifled world. It was a time of increasing economic affluence with more women entering the workforce. Having to work and look after a home and family was not considered a particularly desirable option at that time and it was certainly a lot less common for middle class women to work than it is today. Generally it was assumed that it was better to be at home if you had a family, but lots of women were wearing themselves out juggling home and work life to increase the family income. The efficient household appliances that we have today were not available, and considerably more time was spent on household chores. These women often looked exhausted on admission to hospital. Although they were all in varying degrees of discomfort and pain, they seemed grateful to be waited upon. It must have been a welcome rest for a lot of them.

The ward was so quiet; most of the patients were in bed resting or asleep as I walked around looking for a member of staff.

"Can I help you, Nurse?" asked Sister Burgess, as she quietly emerged from the treatment room.

"Yes, Sister, I am reporting for night duty," I replied, straightening my apron as I stood to attention, in the hope of making a good impression.

Sister Burgess was tall, straight-backed, with the most impeccable posture. She carried her uniform well. Her long blonde hair was neatly tied in a bun underneath her cap. She had such a natural attitude of authority and grace. She was an experienced Ward Sister who had worked on the gynaecology ward for many years. She looked at me with piercing blue eyes for a moment before replying. "Go to the nurses' station and I will be with you shortly to give the report."

Two other nurses soon join me: Nurse Julie Gatenby, a first year student, and Auxiliary Nurse Susan Myers. Nurse Gatenby is on her first year night duty. She is an unhealthy looking specimen, very pale and thin with crooked teeth. She looks terrified and is visibly shaking. Hopefully she will soon settle down. Nurse Myers in contrast is a motherly figure, a plump lady with bright red cheeks and a big smile. Usually there are only two nurses working on each ward at night: an extra pair of hands will be very useful. Sister Burgess arrives as I stand with notebook and pen to scribble down as much information as possible. We all listen intently as she quickly gives the ward report. How was I going to find time to memorise all these patients? I needed to know their names, diagnosis and treatment for the ward round tomorrow morning. It seemed an impossible task as female wards are hard physical work.

The bedpan round alone is a two nurse job, usually assigned to the junior nurses, being performed several times daily, including evenings before patients are settled for the night and first thing in the morning. It is very time-consuming as two nurses are usually required to lift the patient onto the bedpan. It feels like a physical workout as some of the bodies are very heavy. Once everyone is enthroned, it's back to the beginning to lift the patients off. The bedpans were made of a re-usable plastic shell with a disposable lining; fortunately stainless steel bedpans were no longer used. The bedpan disposal unit sits in the sluice; it is inadvisable to switch it on during the night as it is so noisy. Today fully disposable bedpans are becoming available, which are better from an infection control perspective and save nurses' time in cleaning and drying and relieve the problem of storage.

The realisation that I was in charge of the ward felt surreal as I watched the day staff leave. I suddenly felt so alone. I had occasionally been left in charge in my second year, but it had been on day duty with lots of senior staff around. This experience felt very different with much more responsibility, and would last for three months. How was I going to cope?

Susan must have read my thoughts. "Don't worry; I have been working on the ward for over a year now. I know most of the patients and the general routine of the ward. I will help as much as possible." Her smiling face immediately made me feel more relaxed. I organised Julie and Susan to do the evening drinks, the dreaded bedpan round and beds and backs, which relieved me to do observations and treatments. Sister Hunter, the Night Sister, arrived at ten to give out the medicines plus sleeping pills. She was a very stern old school character whom I found to be very intimidating and unfortunately I had to do the medicine round with her. I was certainly kept on my toes as she fired questions at me about every drug we gave out, asking what they were prescribed for, their action and possible side effects.

I felt exhausted when we had finished. After checking the sedatives to account for the amount we had administered and ensure we were left with the correct amount, we signed the drug book and she swiftly left the ward. We had given out lots of sedation, so hopefully the patients would sleep well and enable us to have a quiet night.

Eventually the ward settles down and the lights are turned off, leaving a dim glow of night-lights. I am already feeling tired, my body clock is telling me that I should also be tucked up in bed. The three of us manage a quick cup of tea and a chat. Although complete strangers, I already feel that we will get along and work well together. Julie has noticeably relaxed under the influence of Susan, but like me, looks to be wilting already. Susan, however, looks bright eyed and full of energy. It is obvious she is used to working nights. Around midnight I send them both for a break. I have experience of being alone on the ward at night and can always bleep Sister Hunter if needed. I walk round the ward with my torch, checking on the patients and attempting to memorise their names, diagnosis, treatment and progress for the ward round in the morning.

The night wears on. We are kept busy cleaning and giving out bedpans (much easier on the male wards giving out urinals), making warm drinks for patients who are unable to sleep, checking drips and catheters. It is hard graft.

Around 4am, Julie and I look dreadful. We are struggling to keep awake. "Come with me Julie, let's go to the changing room to wash our faces with cold water and try to spruce ourselves up. Susan can make us a brew as she looks as bright as she did when she arrived at work."

It is 4. 30am. I am busy writing the ward report. Dawn is breaking; the birds are beginning to sing and patients are beginning to stir. I soon begin to feel more alert as the morning routine begins. In addition to the general routine work, I have numerous dressings and swabbings to do.

Even patients who had only had a dilatation and curettage (D&C) had a short spell of bed rest in the sixties. They had to routinely have their vulva swabbed to prevent infection. The first patient requiring the procedure was Sheila. She was only seventeen years old and had unfortunately found herself pregnant after having sex with her boyfriend for the first time. Her parents were devastated and had decided it would be better to abort the baby. Sheila looked very frail and vulnerable. She had been very tearful during the night and I couldn't help feeling deeply sorry for her. She'd had a D&C the previous day. I gently swabbed her vulval area with antiseptic solution, remembering to swab from front to back to prevent re-infecting the area. It was unlike today when a D&C is usually a day case, requiring minimal hands-on nursing care.

In those days D&C was commonly used as a diagnostic procedure for gynaecological conditions, and removal of abnormal growths such as fibroids and polyps, but was also the most often used method of abortion in early pregnancy. Today medical and non-invasive methods exist; because D&C has higher risks of complication the procedure has been declining as a method of abortion.

Andrea was another patient. She had suffered heavy periods for a long time with severe pain and stomach cramps which was having a significant impact on her quality of life. She was pale and very tired. She was twenty-seven and already had four children, so she felt her family was complete. She'd had a hysterectomy two days previously and her wound required re-dressing. She was very emotional.

Both patients, like many others on the ward, desperately needed someone to listen and to talk to, but I was far too busy rushing about to give them my time. Their physical wounds should heal well, but what about their emotional state? What care would they both receive on discharge? Would Sheila's termination be forgotten and never discussed as if it had never happened? Would she have to carry the scars throughout her life? Would Andrea return home and be immediately expected to carry on as normal being a wife and mother of four children? I could only hope that members of their families and friends would be supportive. Sadly, counselling was not as readily available as it is today.

Sister Hunter appeared promptly at six in the morning to do the ward and medicine round. It appeared to go well but it was hard to tell if she was satisfied. Thanks to Susan we were organised by the time the day staff arrived at 7. 30, looking fresh and smart in their clean uniforms. I glanced at Julie who was so tired she could barely stand. "You two are free to go now; I will be following you as soon as I've given the report to the day staff. Many thanks for all your help. Go straight to bed, Nurse Gatenby, and get a good sleep, I will see you tonight when we have to do it all again," I said.

Thoroughly exhausted I skipped breakfast, went straight back to the nurses' home, had a hot bath, fixed my blackout to the window and with my useless earplugs in place fell into bed.

Following a restless day's sleep, I dragged myself out of bed at three-thirty, unable to sleep any longer; thoughts were going round and round in my head. *Would Barbara be okay? How was I going to survive three months of night duty when I felt so tired after working one night?* A glance in the mirror didn't improve my mood. A very pale, puffy red-eyed person stared back at me. I took down my blackout, pulled back the curtains and opened my window to a glorious sunny day. It felt refreshing as the warm breeze entered my hot, stuffy room.

I was eating a large sandwich and drinking a mug of strong tea when Barbara arrived to wake me up.

"Oh, you're awake already. Gosh you look awful. Are you sure you want to come with me?" she asked.

"Of course I do. Once I have eaten this sandwich I should feel a bit better. I don't know what meal I want but I have been starving all day and haven't managed to sleep much. I think my body clock is confused, it must be telling me that I should be awake and eating. I find it difficult to adapt to night duty. What bus do you want to catch?"

"The five o'clock should be okay. We will be there in plenty of time," she replied. Barbara didn't seem worried at all. We chatted and laughed as usual, as she waited for me to get ready.

"You might look a bit better with some make-up on. Do you want to try some of mine?" she asked with a big grin on her face. "It will brighten you up."

"No thanks. I don't trust you. I have to work tonight and I doubt your make-up comes off easily. Some pale eye shadow and lipstick is all I am wearing. I know it will remove easily."

It turned out to be our last journey together on the top deck of a bus. Barbara was pregnant to Harry, her long suffering boyfriend, and left the hospital the following month. She had become such a dear friend to me, I missed her dreadfully.

I became quite depressed during that night duty. I was lacking sleep and finding difficulty concentrating. I was studying when I could and my social life had become non-existent. I reluctantly visited the GP who prescribed sleeping tablets which helped a little. Fortunately, Susan was working with me most nights: she understood how I was feeling and somehow managed to keep me going.

Barbara and Harry soon married. They had a beautiful baby girl called Ella whom they adored. I was amazed how easily Barbara adapted to married life – she didn't appear to miss the hectic social whirl at all. Her son James was born two years later. They were such a happy family. We communicated for many years, and I visited Barbara and her family from time to time, but sadly we eventually lost touch.

# Chapter 23

It was the most perfect autumn day. We were having a spell of dry weather, the sky was clear, but there was a slight chill in the air. I had woken feeling refreshed following a restful night's sleep. Relieved to have completed the dreaded night duty, my body clock had recovered and I was beginning to feel more alive again. It was late September and we were in our last study block. The late starts and early finishes suited me much better as I was more of a mid-morning person. The study block had a relaxed feel about it; no Consultant lectures and no exams at the end. We were, however, aware that the final exams would be soon upon us. The tutors prepared lots of theory and practical revision and attempted to get us thinking and acting like qualified nurses.

It felt good to be together again as a group. We had come such a long way, it was unbelievable that we had reached this stage. Ann was eager to qualify: she hoped to gain experience as a Staff Nurse before leaving to do her midwifery training. Mary remained full of enthusiasm, also keen to qualify; she hoped to get a job in the hospital where she now felt really settled. Linda had lost her ambition of becoming a Nurse Tutor; she hadn't really enjoyed nursing, but as she had managed to come so far, she wanted to get the qualification. She didn't see herself remaining in the profession for long. It seemed such a waste after all the hard work.

I would stay a while to gain some experience, hopefully on a medical ward, but was unsure about what might follow. Bridget couldn't care less what she did! My social life was gradually improving although I hadn't had a boyfriend for a while. Being in block we had evenings free, although we were expected to use the time for studying. Bridget had other ideas! We would often go in a group around the pubs during the week and to the disco on a weekend. Ann didn't join us; she was more mature and sensible than the rest of us, and probably would have been horrified at our behaviour.

I was desperately missing Barbara, from the fun and laughter we had together to the serious conversations and support we offered each other. The image of her with backcombed hair way above her head, thick make-up, short skirt, trying to walk on her killer heels, continued to make me smile. Fortunately, Bridget had a fun-loving personality and was filling some of the gap. Study block soon came to an end. It was the last time we would be together as a group; it was a sad feeling. We would soon be taking different paths in our lives.

Soon December was upon us again. The weather was miserable with dark heavy skies and bitter cold. I felt even more depressed when I saw my off duty schedule on the male surgical ward; I was working both Christmas Day and Boxing Day. I was dreading it.

# *Chapter 24*

"Hello, Nurse Clark. It is lovely to be working with you again." I was pleased to see the soft voice belonged to Sister Frost. She now wore her hair in a short neat style and was wearing a dark blue uniform. She gave me a warm smile and the day suddenly appeared much brighter.

"Hello, Sister Frost. I hardly recognised you with your new hair-do and uniform. Congratulations on your promotion to Senior Sister," I replied.

"Thank you. It seems such a long while since we worked on ward 1. I can't believe you have almost completed your training. Are you enjoying it?" she asked.

"Yes, most of it, but it has been such hard work. I will be glad to get the dreaded final exams out of the way."

"I'm sure you will be fine. It will be worth it in the end. Once you are qualified it will open up lots of career opportunities."

Sister Frost's seniority didn't seem to have changed her; she was as friendly as ever, unlike Charge Nurse Wood who was giving the report. I felt relieved that he would be finishing his shift at five. He was a spindly looking character, his hair was thinning at the front; but his eyes were bright blue, his nose fine, and if you could manage to ignore his silly sticky out ears he could look quite attractive. He enjoyed showing his authority but I soon learnt to focus on his ears and ignore him when he was shouting at me. Fortunately I had passed the stage of being intimidated by such characters.

The shift went smoothly under the direction of Sister Frost as she was so organised. Everyone knew exactly what they were doing and the team worked well together. I left work that evening feeling relaxed and happy; I was working with Sister Frost again the following morning.

The frost lay thickly on the ground as I slid across to the hospital, wrapped warmly in my large woollen cape. I arrived early on the ward to find Sister Frost had been there for a while. The ward was hectic with night staff rushing about. Staffing levels had become a problem as there was a flu epidemic and a large number of staff were on sick leave.

"Good morning, Nurse Clark. I am afraid there are just the two of us on this morning. The four nurses that should be working with us have contracted flu," Sister Frost informed me calmly.

How were we going to cope? Fortunately there wasn't a theatre list today, but how were two nurses going to do the work of six? My immediate response was to panic! Night staff gone, we were left with a ward full of patients needing our care. Sister Frost suggested we sit down while she wrote down the list of things she needed me to do; each chore was carefully timed and we would meet at certain times to do the work that required two nurses. She even insisted I took my full morning break while she did the Consultant's round. When lunchtime arrived all the work was up to date. Sister Frost was happily serving the patients' lunch when the late shift arrived. She was incredible. I was so full of admiration for her and aspired to be like her when I qualified.

That Christmas I travelled home with a bag full of presents for my family. The bus chugged along in its usual fashion. I was wrapped up warm against the cold weather. The countryside was a sad picture, everywhere looked dark, the trees were bare, and the animals reluctantly grazed in the fields. I felt saddened that I would be unable to be with the family over Christmas. It was going to be a very lonely time for me, especially as most of my friends were working different shifts. It would be difficult to spend time together.

Our house looked very smart when I arrived. It was obvious that Mum had been scrubbing the front step and washing the net curtains. The front room was very inviting; Dad had also been very busy putting up the Christmas tree and decorations. The dining table had been laid with the best cutlery and crockery; Mum was preparing a special family meal for me. The warmth from the fire completed the welcome scene. How lucky I was to have such caring parents.

Fortunately my dad was able to take me back the following evening as I had lots of presents to take with me. I wondered if being alone in your room on Christmas Day opening presents was part of the calling that Mum spoke about.

I woke early on Christmas Day morning. It was a dark, cold, windy day. The corridor outside was very quiet. I was on late shift so had plenty of time to open my presents. It was such a lonely time. I was unable to contact my parents as they didn't have a home telephone. How I missed being with my friends and family.

I reluctantly strolled up to the ward. Most of the patients had been discharged which was an advantage as I was in charge of the shift. I couldn't believe my eyes as I pushed the door open. What a wonderful reception. The ward was bright and cheerful. Christmas carols were playing, it had such a festive feel. It was open visiting so the ward was full of people roaming about. It was customary for the Consultant to serve the patients' lunch on Christmas Day. What a sight to see him plating up the food while wearing his smart suit and tie. He was laughing and joking: perhaps he did have a softer side. One of the side wards had been prepared for the staff. It looked very Christmassy, brightly decorated, with plenty of food and drink. Maybe working at Christmas wasn't so bad after all! Boxing Day was equally enjoyable. Work was cut to a minimum and everyone seemed happy. I was on early shift and managed to get off duty early. What a long evening. By seven o'clock I had eaten, pottered about and read and I was desperate for someone to talk to. I headed for the lounge: surely there would be people watching television? But it was in darkness. I switched on the TV and curled up on a chair for a night's viewing. The footsteps rushing past the lounge and along the corridor hesitated for a short while before returning.

"What are you sitting there for Molly? Don't you know it's Christmas?" I swivelled around to see Bridget's smiling face.

"Hello Bridget, I didn't realise it was you. Are you going to join me? I could do with some company," I replied.

"No, definitely not. A few of us are going out to the disco. Why don't you join us? You can't sit here on your own. Hurry up and get ready. We are meeting outside in half-an-hour," she said, glancing at her watch. "Make sure you're not caught; the warden is on the prowl."

"Okay, it will be better than sitting here. See you soon," I replied.

Inappropriately dressed for the cold night air, I managed to escape from the nurses' home and stood outside shivering in the dark. It was not long before the others arrived. The ice-cold wind now contained spits of rain as we ran for the bus. A large queue had already formed when we arrived so we were unable to get under the shelter at the bus stop. Fortunately we had only a short time to wait before the bus arrived. We were barely on the bus when the conductor rang the bell and with a belch of diesel fumes the bus set off. We scrambled to the top deck so the smokers amongst us could have a quick puff. I am sure the conductor enjoyed watching us struggling up the steps in our stiletto heeled shoes.

We were all damp and windswept when we arrived at Lord Jim's, heading straight to the cloakroom to make ourselves look more presentable. It was already ten-thirty and the disco was packed full with young people enjoying themselves. The room was dimly lit, loud music played, groups of girls were dancing around their handbags, and the lads had formed a large queue at the bar. Early hours the following morning found Bridget and me slumped quietly in a corner, drunk and exhausted. Some of the girls had already left as they were on an early shift. Such a minor detail didn't bother Bridget, who would happily party all night and go straight on shift without having had any sleep. Through the cigarette smoke my eyes focused on three young men at the bar. One in particular took my attention. He was tall, slim and attractive. For a moment I could only register that I recognised him from somewhere, but was unable to place him.

"Can you see those three lads over there?" I asked Bridget, nudging her awake as I pointed to them.

"Yes, what about them?" she grumpily replied.

"The one on the left looks familiar. Do you recognise him?"

"No, I've never seen him before. Why don't you go over and ask him if he knows you?" she replied, slumping back into her chair and closing her eyes.

I sat for a while to compose myself, before gathering the courage to walk over to them. The young man had his back to me, but I reached up and tapped him on the shoulder, saying "Excuse me, don't I know you from somewhere?"

He turned and looked at me with a puzzled expression on his face.

"No, I don't think so. I don't think we have ever met before." He grinned at me. Did he think I was a drunk female trying to pick him up? I started to feel rather embarrassed; how was I going to get out of this situation? But we soon found ourselves in conversation, asking lots of questions about each other, ignored by his two friends.

We chatted for quite a while before we realised where we had met before. Andrew had been a patient on ward 1 at the Old Infirmary with a fractured tibia and fibula when I had worked there at the beginning of my training. He had been in the next bed to Michael. I wasn't dreaming after all! It took Andrew a while to place me as he said I looked so different "dressed". I often found that patients did not recognise me away from the hospital and out of uniform.

Bridget hadn't moved since I left her; she was fast asleep. I had to get her back to the hospital.

"Sorry, I will have to go. My friend over there is on early shift and looks as if she should be in bed. I don't think she is capable of getting back to the nurses' home by herself. She has had far too much to drink," I said, pointing to Bridget. "Yes she does look in a bit of a state. It's a shame you have to leave so soon," he replied.

"It's been good to see you again. Bye." I reluctantly turned to walk away.

He stopped me. "Would you fancy meeting again? Maybe for a drink or a meal," he asked.

It was an offer I couldn't refuse.

# Chapter 25

Two days later found me getting ready for my first date with Andrew. *Why was I feeling so nervous? It wasn't the first date I had ever been on. What if we had nothing in common? Would we have anything to talk about now we were both sober? Will he recognise me? What if he doesn't like me? Should I telephone him and cancel?* It had been such a busy day on the ward with lots of new admissions. Charge Nurse Wood had rushed around all day causing mayhem. Thankfully his ears continued to provide a distraction for me. I felt mentally and physically exhausted and just wanted to have a leisurely bath and curl up in bed.

A faint knock at the door disturbed my thoughts. It was Mary; she had recently moved onto my corridor.

"Hi, just finished my shift; thought I was never going to get off. I haven't seen you for a while so thought I'd call to see how you are. Did you manage to get out over Christmas?" she asked.

"Yes, I went out with Bridget and a few of her friends on Boxing Day. I'm just getting ready to go out with someone I met at Lord Jim's. You will probably remember him, we nursed him on ward 1. He remembers Michael."

"Are you going to tell me who it is?" she asked impatiently. She was surprised when I told her who it was. She thought for a moment before continuing, "Yes, I remember him well.

He had a fractured leg. I didn't like him, found him rather arrogant. He was good looking though."

"Thanks, that doesn't make me feel any better! I am beginning to regret agreeing to meet him. We were both very drunk at the time."

"You are only going for a drink with him and he might be a very nice guy now he's not a patient," she said.

"I have no idea what I'm going to wear, most of my clothes have the Barbara influence! I do have a more sensible skirt, which is longer than the rest, and a jumper that goes well with it. Let me show you."

I pulled the skirt and jumper out of my wardrobe and held them up in front of her.

"What do you think? Are they too frumpy?" I asked.

"I think they look fine. Why are you getting yourself so worked up? You worry far too much. I am off to get changed, will be back shortly to check that you are ready."

The reflection in the mirror was a toned down image of my usual going-out dress code. Barbara would not have been impressed. Mary soon returned, inspected me, and apart from commenting on the amount of make-up I was wearing, said I looked presentable.

"Stop worrying. Just go and enjoy yourself. I will make sure the fire escape is open," she said, pushing me out of the door.

I managed to sneak out of the building. The weather remained bitterly cold but the rain had stopped. The bus soon arrived and I joined the sensible passengers on the lower deck. I didn't want to smell of cigarette smoke before going into the pub, although I was desperate for a cigarette to calm my nerves. Andrew was waiting for me at the bus stop as arranged. He looked rather smart, so I was pleased I had taken Mary's sensible advice on how to dress for a first date. After taking several deep breaths, I managed to compose myself before getting off the bus. He instantly recognised me.

"Hi, you look frozen. We haven't far to walk to the pub," he said.

Andrew's relaxed manner soon transferred to me. The conversation flowed freely as we rushed to the pub, keen to get out of the cold. Andrew was so easy to talk to, very witty and not at all arrogant. Mary wasn't always right!

The evening went by very quickly. I had forgotten how tired I was as we reluctantly left the pub to walk to the taxi rank. It was late and I had missed the last bus back to the hospital. I got into the taxi feeling relaxed and contented. Andrew was unlike my usual type of boyfriend – I had never felt such an attraction before. I had only a short while to wait before our next date.

# Chapter 26

The alarm clock rings. I sit up with a start; surely it can't be Saturday morning already? It was a miserable February morning, bitterly cold with a howling wind. I am tempted to stay in my warm bed and catch up on my sleep, but need to cram in some necessary studying before I start my late shift on male orthopaedics. I have so much to learn before the dreaded final exams and insufficient time left to do the work. It is a while since I have seen Andrew as he is back at college in Leeds. Unfortunately he only comes home at weekends when I am often working. I am hoping to get off duty on time as he is picking me up from the hospital at 10pm. Nursing and dating don't go well together.

The ward has a tranquil feel when I arrive. Weekends tend to be relatively quiet as there are no Consultant rounds or routine theatre patients to organise, which I am pleased about as I am in charge of the shift. I have a good team working with me and everything is running to plan when the telephone rings. We are getting an admission; a young man has been knocked off his bike on his way home from work and has fractured his femur. It is five-thirty when John is admitted with his worried parents who are reassured and shown to the day room until we make him comfortable. John is very distressed and in considerable pain. His bone has been set and needs to be put in a Thomas splint to allow complete rest of the fracture, allowing natural healing to take place with the bone in the proper position. Doctor Mullen, who has just started working on the ward, soon arrives.

"Can I have a word?" he asks. We go into the office. Appearing rather nervous, he continues, "Do you know how to put a Thomas splint on? I know how to do it in theory but I have never put one on before."

"No, I don't. I have never put one on either, but I'm sure we can muddle through it together. The patient in the side ward has one so we can use it as a guide if necessary. I think we need to measure his good leg first to see what size of splint to put on," I reply.

The morphine John was given in casualty is beginning to take effect and he is much calmer. Doctor Mullen measures the length of the good leg and the width of the thigh at the groin, remembering to allow for any swelling. We collect the splint, bandages, strips of cloth and adhesive tape to hold the splint in place and thick, soft padding to allow the injured part to swell and reduce interference with circulation. I maintain traction to the leg while supporting the knee and thigh while Doctor Mullen carefully puts the frame in place. It fits snugly in the groin; John gives a sigh of relief. The splint is suspended using an overhead beam enabling the splint to move freely with him when he moves in bed. We pull the cords through the pulley and finally hang weights on the end to provide continuous traction.

"Well, I think it looks professional, how about you?" I ask Dr Mullen.

"Yes, I think we have done a good job."

"I will just check the one in the side ward to make sure everything is correct." The patient is fast asleep so is unaware as I check his splint. "Do you know what we have forgotten?" I ask Dr Mullen.

"No. Everything looks fine to me," he says, carefully checking the traction once more.

"We have forgotten to elevate the foot of the bed for counter traction. We don't want you shooting out of the bottom of the bed do we John?"

We are all in fits of laughter. John's parents are pleased to see him looking more comfortable.

I have still lots to do before going off duty. I will never be ready for my date. Sister has done the ward round so there shouldn't be any more authoritative figures visiting the ward; dare I pop over to the nurses' home, have a shower and put my make-up on during my supper break? Why not? Barbara used to get away with it! I will then just need to get changed when I go off duty. A few of the patients noticed that I looked more glamorous when I returned from my break. It must have been a strange sight to see a nurse wearing make-up! Andrew was already waiting for me in his dad's car. Feeling very excited, with butterflies in my tummy, I tottered out of the hospital grounds to join him. He was waiting in a secluded area away from the street lamps so I wouldn't be seen. How do you get into a car in ladylike fashion wearing five inch heels and a very short skirt? Andrew didn't seem to notice as he gave me a kiss on the cheek. It is four in the morning as I scramble up the fire escape. I am on early shift and the alarm will ring at six-thirty. I feel wide awake but am sure I will start to wilt before my shift is over. Unlike Bridget, I do need my rest.

I find it difficult to concentrate as Mr Carter, the Consultant, appears on the ward with his team. Dr Mullen is also struggling to keep his eyes open but for different reasons; he has been on call all night. The housemen are frequently on call for twenty-four hours a day, with only one day off a week. How do they cope with the lack of sleep? We gather around John's bed. Mr Carter quietly surveys the traction.

"Who has put this traction up?" he asks. Dr Mullen looks at me and says nothing. "It was Dr Mullen and me," I reply sheepishly.

Mr Carter smiles at us both. "Well done, it is perfect," he says, gently patting me on the back. Fortunately, John doesn't mention what a hassle it was and how we had forgotten to elevate the bed. . . . . .

Andrews's parents invited me for an overnight stay with them during his February half term. I was very excited as my twenty-first birthday was in the same week and couldn't wait to tell Mum. Her reaction was not as I had expected.

"I'm not happy about these arrangements. You haven't known him very long and you don't know anything about his family," she said. I accepted she was concerned about me but I was almost twenty-one and had a very responsible job. But Andrew's mum wrote to her explaining that they were keen to meet me and I would be well looked after. She eventually agreed.

It was the best birthday ever. Although his parents initially appeared rather posh, they gave me a very warm welcome. Andrew had a brother and I think they enjoyed having another female in the house. Following a good night's sleep, I woke to a crisp, cold day, the sky was bright blue, the sun shone and a fine dusting of snow lay on the ground. We celebrated my birthday with lunch at the Castle Hill pub. The warmth of the pub was very inviting after walking up the hill. Having lunch with lots of wine was such a treat. I slipped on the ice on the way back but was so drunk I didn't feel a thing. We had a good laugh as Andrew pulled me to my feet. It had been a perfect day.

# Chapter 27

I was feeling apprehensive as I starting work on the intensive care unit. I had never set foot in the place before. I found myself in a sterile environment, with a large ratio of staff to patients. The patients were all suffering with the most severe and life-threatening illnesses and injuries which required constant close monitoring and support from specialist equipment and medications. The staff were highly trained doctors and nurses who specialised in caring for seriously ill patients.

Beds were surrounded by medical equipment. The staff quietly attended to their patients, and only the faint sound of the monitors could be heard. I was completely overwhelmed by my surroundings. Although I was a confident student nurse, I felt very much out of my comfort zone.

Sister Scott greeted me with a smile showing her perfect set of white teeth. She was quite young and very pretty with short jet black hair and attractive blue eyes. She had a gentle air about her which was reminiscent of Sister Frost. Hopefully she wouldn't be too harsh or expect my standard of work to reflect the two blue stripes on my hat! How much more did I need to learn before qualifying?

There were six patients on the ward, all with different illnesses. I would be assisting Sister Scott in the care of a patient who had suffered a severe stroke. It was a relief to learn that a qualified member of staff would always be with me.

Mrs Arthur was a middle aged lady who had been admitted two days previous. She was deeply unconscious. The right side of her face was terribly twisted as though muscles had been pulled with a wire. Her mouth was dragged to one side and her eye drooped. There were numerous tubes taped to her, a needle in her arm and machinery surrounding her bed.

It was such an upsetting sight, I could feel the tears welling up. Sister Scott introduced me, talking to Mrs Arthur as if she was conscious. As we were giving her a bed bath and making her comfortable, I realised I had nursed her on the medical ward a while ago following a heart attack. She had recovered well at that time and was discharged home to her family. It was so sad to see her in this condition.

I chatted to her in the hope that she would recognise my voice but there was no response. I was amazed how busy we were just caring for one patient; washing, pressure area care, tube feeding, changing drips and catheter bags, frequent observations and administering medications. We were able to provide excellent nursing care which I found very rewarding. Mrs Arthur never re-gained consciousness and peacefully died several days later.

I settled on the unit very quickly, the staff were helpful and the work was interesting. Each patient had a different condition, you could be nursing a patient following a severe trauma one day, then a patient with multiple organ failure the next. This valuable experience would take me up to the final exams.

I only nursed Steven for several days but I will always remember him. He was seventeen, a previously healthy young man who had returned from his day's work feeling unwell, complaining of a severe headache. During his evening meal he started to feel sick, left the table and went upstairs to the bathroom. When a good length of time passed and he didn't return, his mum went upstairs to find him unconscious on the bathroom floor. He had suffered a massive brain haemorrhage and was admitted to our unit shortly afterwards where he was put on a life support machine. The consultant sympathetically prepared his parents for the worse. They sat holding his hands when the ventilator was disconnected. They were distraught. It was so upsetting. I still found death very difficult to cope with, but the death of a young person in such tragic circumstances was unbearable. I gained a wealth of experience while working on the ICU. I was able to use the clinical and caring skills I had been taught. As the patients were desperately ill, I frequently had to hold a dying patient's hand with sadness and dignity, caring for that patient in their final moments. I learnt how important end of life care is. I still found the death of a patient very upsetting and continued to shed many tears. I had great respect for the dedicated staff working in such a stressful environment.

## Chapter 28

I woke shortly after dawn. Early rays streamed into my bedroom. I was unable to sleep. I sat, deep in thought, on the edge of the bed running my toes through the carpet tuft. It was the day of my final results. The exams felt to have gone reasonably well at the time; even the practical hadn't been too bad and I had confidently answered all the questions asked by the examiners. What if I had failed after three years' hard slog?

I quickly got dressed, had a strong cup of tea and a cigarette and rushed downstairs to learn my fate. The room was full. Some of the students had already opened their envelopes and it was evident not all had received good news.

"Hi Molly. Have you got through?" said Bridget with a big smile on her face.

"I don't know yet. I've just arrived. I gather you have passed by the expression on your face."

"Yes. I can't believe it. Must be right as I've read it three times."

"Congratulations, you must be relieved."

"Never mind me. Hurry up and collect your envelope."

Bridget watched with anticipation as I slowly opened the envelope.

"Hurry up. You won't change the contents by opening it so slowly," she said shaking her head and laughing.

I pulled out the letter and started to read:

*Dear Madam,*

*I have much pleasure in informing you that your application for registration has been approved and your name has now been entered on the part of the register for General Nurses maintained by the General Nursing Council for England and Wales. Your registration number is 412808 and you are now entitled to call yourself a Registered Nurse; your date of registration is 30th July 1969.*

*Your certificate of registration will be forwarded in due course to your permanent address; I would however point out that the certificate has to be engrossed and sealed, and some time must therefore elapse before it is ready to be issued. In the meantime, you may use this letter as evidence of your registration having been effected.*

*A uniform permit is enclosed herewith. Your State Registered Badge will be sent to you direct from the manufacturers, but as each badge is engraved with the name, registration number, and date of registration of the owner, there is likely to be a delay of approximately six months before it can be issued. When you receive the badge great care should be taken of it in order that it may not fall into the hands of any unauthorised person; it is the property of the council and arrangements should be made for its return to these offices on the death of a nurse. The loss of a badge should be notified at once.*

"Well, have you passed then?" Bridget asked impatiently.

"Yes, look," I replied handing her the letter as tears of relief and joy started to run down my cheeks. I was pleased to hear that Ann, Mary and Linda had also passed but sad that several of the girls had failed. I couldn't begin to imagine how they were feeling; it seemed wrong to celebrate.

"I'm off to the sewing room to get measured for my uniform. Are you coming?" Bridget asked.

"Yes, I'll come, with you but I'm not waiting if there's a long queue as it's my day off and I can't wait to get home and tell Mum and Dad the good news."

"Do you think we can ask for the length to be a bit shorter now we are Staff Nurses?"

"You must be joking! I doubt it but you can always ask," I replied.

I managed to get measured for my new uniform before catching the bus home.

The bus had the same rhythm and sound as any other time I had made the journey but it felt different. Was it because I didn't have my head in a textbook? What a beautiful summer morning, not a cloud in the sky. I felt so relaxed looking out of the window. A Staff Nurse at last. Maybe Mum was right and I had been called to become a nurse after all.

Mum was sitting in the back garden reading the paper when I arrived. She was so pleased to see me.

"Hi Mum, how are you?"

"Not too bad. I'm just having a few minutes to myself before going to work. I didn't expect you until this afternoon."

"No, I thought it would be later but I'm glad I managed to catch the earlier bus as I've got something to show you and will need to get back to the hospital tomorrow morning." I handed Mum the letter.

She quietly read it then looked at me and said, "I always knew you could do it, well done." It was good to see Mum happy and smiling. She had been very upset for months as our street was soon for demolition. We had all found such happiness living in that house. I was born there, and had such a happy childhood. My parents often struggled to make ends meet, but always managed to provide well for their family; we wanted for nothing, although they often went without.

"Hurry up Molly. Your bus leaves in an hour and you haven't had any breakfast yet," Mum shouted loudly up the stairs. I smiled to myself as I was reminded of my school days when I was reluctant to get out of bed. Mum needed to do a lot of shouting up the stairs in order to waken me. It was usually the third shout that eventually got me out of bed. It was fortunate the school was just a short walk away.

I hurriedly got ready and with only minutes left ran down the street and jumped on the bus as it was slowly pulling out of the station. "Oh you be careful love. You're lucky you haven't injured yourself," said the conductor, grabbing my arm and helping me to my seat. I was so eager to return to the hospital and collect my uniform.

Bridget shouted to me as she rushed back to the hospital after her morning break. "Have you collected your uniform yet?"

"No, just on my way to get it now. You look very smart in yours."

"Thanks. It's no shorter than my student uniform but the colour is good. Better hurry. Don't want to be late back on the ward. Must set a good example to the students. Catch up with you later."

Fully dressed in my purple dress with a wide purple strip on my cap, I glanced in the mirror. Bridget was right, the dress was long but the colour was good and it really suited me. It was my first day as a Staff Nurse on the female surgical ward. I had already been working on the ward and knew the patients well. Would they recognise me? The ward was filled with endless chatter and laughter; as usual Lil's voice could be heard way above the rest. Mrs Lilly Badger, known to friends as Lil, was a typical stoic middle aged Yorkshire woman of the sixties. She was such a character, resourceful, obstinate, with irrepressible good humour. Being stone deaf, she tended to shout, making it impossible to have a discreet conversation with her. She was the first to notice me, so the news travelled fast.

"Hey, has anyone seen Nurse Clark? Doesn't she look smart in her new uniform? We will have to behave ourselves now she is a Staff Nurse." The neighbouring patients, enjoying the banter, started to congratulate me. I was bursting with pride.

"Thank you ladies. Lil is right though, you will have to behave yourselves now, although I have only another week to work on the ward before going on holiday to the coast with my friend for a much needed break."

"Won't you be coming back to this ward?" asked Lil.

"No, I will be working on male medical. It should be easier than looking after you lot. I'd better go and do some work, haven't time to stand here talking. Back shortly to change your dressing, Lil," I said.

Poor Lil had spent a miserable few months suffering with her gall bladder. She had coped well with the pain but was not happy being unable to eat her usual diet. Lil loved her food, which was reflected in her size; she was almost as wide as she was tall. *I can't wait to get back to eating properly,* she would frequently say. She felt cheated if she didn't have her fried breakfast plus plenty of unhealthy snacks during the day. Any advice on healthy eating was ignored. Lil was making a good recovery following a cholecystectomy. She was eager to return home and be able to enjoy her food without suffering any pain now the offending organ had been removed.

"Right Lil, let's see what state this wound of yours is in," I said, pulling the curtains round her bed.

"What's it like, Staff Nurse? she asked.

"Give me a chance to get the old dressing off first Lil. I'm being as quick as I can." The dressing was barely removed before she was asking if it was healing. It was impossible to concentrate.

"It's looking good Lil. Healing really well. You will be home eating your healthy diet before you know it," I said jokingly. Lil had the art of extracting personal information from you without you realising. She knew all about Andrew; that he was working in Jersey during his summer holidays and we communicated daily by letter. Not surprisingly it didn't take long for the news to travel around the ward. It soon became a source of great interest amongst the patients. *Have you had a letter this morning Staff Nurse? What has he got to say? When is he coming home? I bet you can't wait to see him. I bet he is missing you.* My love life had somehow become a major topic of interest, no doubt providing some light relief for many of the patients. Lil was soon discharged home leaving the ward a much quieter place.

Andrew was uppermost in my mind as I packed my suitcase ready for my holiday with Ann. How I missed him. Life seemed so lonely without him. I was desperate to see him again.

# Chapter 29

The train chugged slowly out of the station. Was our holiday over already? The week had flown by. Ann and I had spent a wonderful time together by the coast. The weather had been hot and sunny enabling us to spend lots of leisure time outdoors. There was still life outside the hospital! Feeling much healthier, with colour in our cheeks, we felt ready to return to work.

The train was full of young families also leaving their holidays behind, so it was noisy with excited children jumping around. The journey gradually became quieter as they disembarked at stops along the way. I was beginning to feel very sleepy, finding it impossible to keep my eyes open. The swaying movement of the train was not helping matters. "It's too late to fall asleep now. We should arrive in Huddersfield in around ten minutes," Ann said, lightly kicking my leg.

"Sorry Ann. I didn't mean to ignore you. Train journeys always affect me like this. I have really enjoyed my holiday. Thanks for asking me to join you."

"Yes, I've enjoyed it as well. The sea air always makes me feel better. I wonder what life will be like as a Staff Nurse."

"Don't know. Rather stressful I should imagine with all the added responsibility, but I'm sure we'll manage. I am looking forward to starting on male medical."

"I bet you are. I am pleased that I am working on geriatrics, I enjoy nursing the elderly. We were so lucky to get the wards we wanted," she replied. The train soon arrived at Huddersfield. "Come on. Back to reality. At least we have a day off tomorrow to get organised," said Ann.

The platform was very busy with people milling around. Jumping off the train I saw a young man smiling at us. He looked like Andrew but surely it couldn't be? I must be dreaming. He wasn't due back from Jersey for a while yet. The realisation soon dawned on me as he started to walk towards us. It *was* Andrew. He looked so handsome and here I was, tired and scruffy after a long train journey. "Hi, it's so good to see you again. I've got Dad's car so thought I'd meet you off the train and give you a lift back to the hospital," he said, giving me a big hug.

"Oh thanks," I said, staring at him in disbelief. "I'm speechless. I didn't expect to see you for a few weeks."

"I decided to come home early as I was missing you so much."

Ann was looking very confused as she listened to the conversation. "Sorry Ann. I didn't mean to ignore you. Can I introduce you to Andrew?"

"Pleased to meet you Andrew. I have heard so much about you," said Ann, shaking his hand with a huge grin on her face.

We soon arrived back at the hospital. Ann thanked him, collected her suitcase and left to unpack. I couldn't stop smiling, it felt surreal. We arranged to meet that evening for a meal to celebrate my exam results.

"Pick you up around seven-thirty-ish, Staff Nurse," he shouted as he drove off.

Life was good. I had a wonderful boyfriend who I adored and a job that I was very settled in. It was my first day working as a qualified nurse on the male medical ward. How fortunate I was to be working on my favourite ward. Sister Bennett was in charge of the shift. We had previously met when I was working nights on the ward at the beginning of my second year. Sister Bennett was Junior Sister on day duty then. She was now Senior Sister, the dark blue uniform accentuating her beautiful red hair.

"Hello, Staff Nurse Clark. I was pleased to hear you would be joining us. You are working the same shifts as me over the next two days. It will give you chance to familiarise yourself with the routine of the ward before you are left in charge," she said.

"Oh, thank you Sister. That will be helpful. I am feeling rather anxious at being responsible for administering drugs and being in charge of the drug cupboard keys."

"Don't worry. You will soon get used to it. It is a huge responsibility, but if in doubt there are always doctors and senior nursing staff around to help."

It was the dreaded Consultant's round that morning. The patients were neatly in bed, hardly daring to move, covered by crisp white sheets. Mr Harris arrived with his brusque manner, dressed smartly in his suit with his hair neatly styled with lots of Brylcreem. He rushed down the ward, his junior doctors in their starched white coats, the physiotherapist and dietician all trailing behind.

I felt nervous as Sister Bennett introduced me. "Good morning Sir. This is our new Staff Nurse. She has just started on the ward this morning."

Mr Harris scarcely looked at me as he made a grunting sound. He certainly knew how to make you feel welcome! The ward round was a sober affair. Patients sat quietly while their conditions were discussed as if it didn't concern them. Mr Harris would raise his voice to Sister if X-ray and blood test results weren't immediately available. He would humiliate staff if they were unable to answer his questions, frequently using the word incompetent.

The poor housemen; how did they manage to tolerate the man? They worked so hard. Some of them would have been on call the previous night before having to endure such an ordeal. They spent much of the day working on the ward. Mr Harris always left them plenty of work to do. A common task for housemen at that time was to draw blood. Nowadays most hospitals hire and train phlebotomists for the job.

My confidence quickly grew. I had gained a vast amount of knowledge during my training, but was soon to realise how much more I had to learn.

I was in charge on the day Dan was admitted to the ward. He was a young man in his late teens. I was shocked by his appearance. I had never seen anything like it; what was wrong with him? He looked extremely ill. He was bloated as if he had been blown up like a balloon. His face was round and bright red. His skin appeared thin with areas of bruising.

"Hello Dan. I'm Staff Nurse Clark. You will need to get changed into your pyjamas and get into bed before the doctor comes to examine you. Can you manage or would you like some help?" I asked.

"I think I will be able to manage but might need some help. I feel so tired," he replied in a weak voice.

"I will pop back shortly to see how you're doing."

I soon returned to a pitiful sight. Dan was struggling to get changed. His body was that of a much older person. He was covered in large reddish-purple stretch marks.

"Hi Dan, it's only me. How are you doing? Shall I give you a hand?" I asked.

"Please if you would. I am so slow."

"We will have you comfortable in bed in no time." Dan was so heavy I had to get assistance getting him into bed.

"I just need to do your observations before the doctor arrives. Then we will leave you to rest." I noted that he had a raised blood pressure.

The houseman was also puzzled by his appearance and called the registrar for his advice. Following examination, it was thought that Dan was displaying the signs and symptoms of Cushing's syndrome, a rare metabolic disorder that was new to me. The registrar explained to us that Cushing's syndrome, also known as hypercortisolism, features a collection of symptoms that develop due to very high levels of the hormone cortisol in the body. People who take high doses of corticosteroids (anti-inflammatory medicines) long term often have a build-up of cortisol in their blood. This however wasn't the case with Dan who had been previously fit and healthy. Blood and urine samples were taken and he was made comfortable in bed.

It was days later before the diagnosis was confirmed. It was the lesser common cause of Cushing's syndrome, where a tumour develops in one of the body's glands causing it to produce an excessive amount of hormones; it was known as endogenous Cushing's syndrome. Dan's parents were relieved that a diagnosis had finally been made. He was transferred to the surgical ward where he had a tumour removed and made a full recovery.

I jumped out of bed early on Thursday 18th September 1969. It was prize giving day for the nursing staff. The hospital had been fully of activity preparing for the event for weeks. I was so excited I hadn't slept a wink. The proceedings didn't start until 3. 15pm which gave me plenty of time to get organised. I was to receive my State Registered Nurse certificate plus prizes for ophthalmology and gynaecology. I had received top marks in two of my worst subjects! Following numerous cups of tea I ironed a clean uniform and hung it ready on the wardrobe. The shoes Mum had bought me at the beginning of my training were polished to a high shine. They still looked new with years of wear still left in them. There was time for a bath and hair wash before meeting Bridget for lunch. Panic! My hair had become totally unruly. I washed and dried it twice with no improvement. It was out of control, with bits sticking out all over the place. I couldn't receive my prizes looking like this! Bridget soon arrived. "What have you done to your hair?" she said, laughing.

"Don't laugh, it's a disaster. I've just washed it and for some reason this is the result. I can't attend prize giving like this, everyone will laugh at me."

"Calm down. Don't be so dramatic. It's only hair and it isn't as bad as you think."

"It must be for you to notice it straight away." I was so upset.

"It's just a bit different, more fly-away than usual. Let's walk up to the hairdressers. She might be able to fix it if she has time."

The hairdresser soon remedied the problem. I was feeling much happier as I left with a neat, shiny hair-do. The room was packed full of proud parents. Mum and Dad were in prime position on the front row. They had taken time off work to attend.

"Hi, you must have arrived early to get the best seats," I said patting Mum on the shoulder.

"Oh Molly, you startled me," she said, turning round. "We arrived earlier than planned. The roads were very quiet."

"Yes we had a good journey and have had time to walk around the hospital grounds and have a cup of tea," said Dad.

"I'd better go, I'm on my way to join the other nurses, but we'll get a chance to have a good natter later."

"Okay, we have a lot of catching up to do. Hope it goes well. See you later," said Dad with a big grin on his face.

Taking up my position amongst a rowdy group of nurses I soon became aware how tired my parents looked. They had recently bought a new semi-detached bungalow and had been busy packing for the house move. They worked so hard. It was because of their help and encouragement that I was sitting here today. I felt such gratitude for what they had done for me.

The proceedings began with the Chairman's opening remarks, followed by Matron's report and the school of nursing report given by Miss Hillman. Speeches from various people followed, including the Chairman of the General Nursing Council for England and Wales, before the presentations began. Mr Bartley had to present me with the gynaecology prize. Would he recognise me as the Nurse who didn't pay attention? He managed a slight smile as he shook my hand and said *Well done Nurse*. Maybe he didn't remember; surely I wasn't the only person to fall asleep in his lectures.

There was much excitement as we walked to the dining room for a celebration tea. Mum and Dad were clearly enjoying the day, meeting some of my nursing friends and their families. The dining room had been set out nicely, where we enjoyed a selection of sandwiches and cakes. Miss Hillman joined us as Mum and Dad were about to leave. She had a long chat with them saying how well I had done and how proud they must be. Receiving praise made me feel rather uncomfortable. I was surprised to hear that I had been selected to have my photograph taken with three other nurses. It would feature with an article on the prize giving in the *Huddersfield Daily Examiner* the following day, Friday 19th September 1969. It had been a perfect day.

# Chapter 30

Was it a dream? I sat up in bed rubbing my eyes. It was very early in the morning, but unable to get back to sleep I rolled slowly out of bed. My certificate and prizes were on my dressing table; so yesterday must have happened. My prizes were book vouchers; surely they didn't expect me to use them for medical books? My brain was in need of a long rest. I was up and dressed with plenty of time to spare. Feeling very hungry, I decided to call in the dining room for a hearty breakfast before arriving on duty.

"I see you're well up the list for prizes, Nurse Clark." I turned to see the unmistakable rear view of Sister Fletcher; a thin upper body with a large wobbly bottom and fat legs. She was busy reading the notice board. With a shrug of her shoulders she continued grudgingly: "I suppose congratulations are in order."

Ignoring her bad manners I replied, "Thank you Sister Fletcher. I am pleased all my hard work has paid off."

We had no further conversation as she followed me into the dining room.

With a full stomach I felt ready for work. What was in store for me today? Each day was so unpredictable, anything could happen. I was finding the ward interesting, continually learning and gaining experience.

The familiar sounds filled the ward; staff rushing around, the clanking of instruments, hissing of oxygen cylinders, beeping of monitors, patients talking, groaning and coughing. Mr Rowen was an elderly gentleman suffering from lung cancer. He had been a patient on the ward for several weeks in a very poorly state. His condition had deteriorated rapidly over the past few days so he had been transferred into a side ward where his family could visit him when they wished. He was having regular injections of morphine for his pain and drifted in and out of consciousness. It was like stepping into a different world as I entered the side ward; it had such a tranquil feel.

His wife and son were sitting quietly by his bedside. She was gently holding his hand with silent tears in her eyes. Bereavement can be a devastating event but the experience is often eased when families have time to prepare for it. Mr Rowen had been ill for many years and the family were aware that he was soon expected to die. What do you say to relatives in this situation?

"He looks so peaceful. Would you like a cup of tea?" I asked, gently touching Mrs Rowen's arm. Why do we offer tea in such circumstances? I never understood, but most people gladly accept.

Mr Rowen passed away a few hours later with his family present. He had not died alone in hospital in the care of strangers, as many patients did. He looked so peaceful, calm and relaxed with his lines and wrinkles smoothed out. There was a feeling of serenity in the room. I felt relieved when close relatives were able to be present when loved ones died in hospital. Mrs Rowen had family and friends who were very supportive and I felt confident they would help her to cope with this emotional crisis, being there when she needed them.

The family soon left and I had the job of laying the body out before going off duty. It was such an important part of nursing, something I had done many times but still found very upsetting. I asked one of the junior nurses to help me and together we respectfully laid the body out. Nurses don't do it any more; these days it is carried out by the mortician.

It was almost six when I left the ward, an hour later than expected. I had arranged to meet Andrew in Huddersfield at seven-thirty. It's surprising how quickly you are able to get ready when you are in love. I had soon forgotten how tired I felt and with butterflies in my tummy ran to catch the bus. Andrew was sitting on a shop windowsill opposite the bus stop reading a newspaper. "Well done. I'm just reading about the prize giving day. You look to be enjoying yourself on the photo, can't wait to hear all about it," Andrew said with a big smile.

"Let me have a look," I said as he handed me the paper. I was pleasantly surprised, even my hair looked good.

"I have booked a table for dinner. Let's go and celebrate." A wonderful evening followed.

Work seemed to be dominating my life. It was often difficult finding time to meet Andrew and we were spending so little time together. I had decided to accept a Staff Nurse post on night duty. I would be working nine nights followed by seven nights off. It sounded very appealing.

Although many of the qualified staff lived outside the hospital, renting property could be expensive. I was happy to stay in the nurses' home enjoying the camaraderie. The strict rules still applied, but you were allowed more late passes after qualifying. Unfortunately this didn't extend to all night. I was now much better off financially. Our pay had to be collected from the wages department at the end of each month where there was often a long queue. We would receive a sealed packet containing a pay slip and the cash. I was now receiving a Staff Nurse pay of around £50 per month, a large increase from the £11 student pay. I shouldn't need to borrow money from Dad any more.

## Chapter 31

A hospital ward is a wonderful place to work at night. There is a feeling of stillness. It is much quieter than during the day with no routine admissions or discharges, the telephone rarely rings and staff numbers are reduced with only two to three nurses working on each ward. With my new bag packed with toiletries, high energy snacks and some light reading, I was well prepared. It was my first night on the medical unit. Fortunately I was familiar with all the patients as I had been doing days on the same ward. I was relieved to be fully staffed as Student Nurse Lang and Nursing Auxiliary Parsons joined me. They were both experienced nurses. Nurse Lang was in her second year, very confident and able. Nurse Parsons was in her early twenties; having worked as an auxiliary for several years she had decided to start nurse training in the near future. Sister Bennett delivered the report and handed me the drug cupboard keys which I pinned securely in my uniform pocket.

Jim, a patient in his mid-fifties who was suffering from early onset dementia, was soon helping, busy serving the night drinks; it was a job he enjoyed. It was good to see how well he coped, pushing the trolley and chatting to the patients as he served their drinks. They didn't always get the drink they had ordered but no one ever complained. Patients all settled, we were hoping for a quiet night. But in the early hours of the morning, when the nurses were having their meal break, I suddenly heard shouting from one of the side wards. Jim had become confused, removed his pyjamas and wandered next door to where Mr Dean was sleeping. Mr Dean had been wakened to the sight of a naked man trying to get in bed with him. I managed to calmly steer Jim back to his bed and settle him down.

Mr Dean was traumatised by the experience, and it took endless cups of tea and lots of reassurance before he was able to settle back to sleep. The following morning Jim was fine, happily going round the ward with the tea trolley, oblivious to his night's behaviour. This pattern of behaviour occurred most nights. Most patients were used to it and were able to ignore the naked outline of Jim passing by in half-light.

I was glad to get off duty and into bed. Why had I chosen to work nights? Drifting off to sleep I was startled by a loud thumping at the door.

"Staff Nurse Clark. You have left the ward with the drug cupboard keys." I opened the door to Sister Brooks, arms folded under her bosom. She stared at me and continued.

"It is extremely important that you pass them over to the qualified person next in charge before you leave the ward. Get dressed and take them back." Did she honestly think I had done it intentionally? I was far too tired to respond.

Mr Tully was a tall, lanky, middle aged gentleman with a very deep voice. He had been in the ward for many weeks receiving treatment for ulcerative colitis. On admission to the ward he had considerable abdominal pain and was very pale and weak. He was initially nursed in bed, having a strict low residue diet to rest the colon. He had been given codeine and belladonna to ease his pain, salazopyrin to help reduce the inflammation and antibiotics, iron and vitamins. This regime had obviously done the trick as he started to look much better and was getting stronger.

Mr Tully was a very likeable chap, popular with everyone. He could be heard each morning, whistling and singing, with his toilet bag and towel tucked under his arm on his way to the bathroom. He always brought a smile to my face, which was often needed in the morning especially after a hard night's work. He would emerge soon afterwards in his clean pyjamas and dressing-gown. "Reporting for duty Staff Nurse Clark. What would you like me to do?" he would ask, standing to attention and saluting. The usual job was to help Jim serving the morning teas.

One evening when the ward was quiet and Mr Tully was playing cards, I decided to put some cornflakes under his bottom sheet. Mr Hinchcliffe, the patient in the next bed, gave me a puzzled look. Smiling at him I explained, "He's always playing tricks on us. See how long it takes him to notice. I hope he doesn't eat them, cornflakes aren't on his diet yet." Mr Tully soon got into bed and fell fast asleep. I checked on the patients hourly throughout the night and Mr Tully was always fast asleep. His bed must feel uncomfortable, hadn't he noticed? I was puzzled. The following morning he was up with the larks following his usual routine with no mention of cornflakes! As I was removing the crushed cornflakes from his mattress, Mr Hinchcliffe didn't look too pleased. "I don't think he noticed. He slept all night, unlike me. All I could hear was *crackle, crackle* every time he moved." I felt dreadful and apologised profusely, hoping he wouldn't mention it to anyone.

"Bye, Staff Nurse Clark. Hope you sleep well. See you tonight," Mr Tully shouted as I left the ward. Back in my room I opened my bag to find it full of cornflakes.

Bernard was well known in the hospital, where he had worked as a porter for many years. He had smoked heavily since his late teens and suffered from emphysema. He had been admitted to the ward in a very poorly state. He was cyanosed, very breathless with a dreadful cough. He was being nursed in the side ward next to the nurses' station where we could keep a close eye on him. He looked so ill, propped up in bed with continuous oxygen to help him breathe. We were checking him hourly to monitor any change. Sadly he wasn't responding well to his antibiotics and steroid tablets. His condition had remained unchanged throughout the night and as he was finding it difficult to sleep, I decided to try to make him comfortable before waking the other patients.

"Good morning Bernard," I said softly, filling a bowl of water for him to wash. "Let me help you have a wash and see if we can get you more comfortable." Bernard didn't respond so I assumed he had fallen asleep. On closer examination he was very still and quiet, the only sound was the oxygen machine. Bernard had died. I was deeply shocked. I had been talking to him a short while ago. I felt responsible, although I knew there was nothing anyone could have done. His time had come. I was saddened that, like many patients, he had died alone.

Some nights we were so short staffed I had to cover other wards as well as working on the medical ward, often leaving a nurse working alone for a while on a busy ward. Nurses always seemed to cope admirably. I had never considered the danger aspect of being alone, until early one morning when I was writing the report. The ward was quiet and the nurse working with me had gone for her break.

Suddenly I became aware of someone standing next to me. It was Mr Leach, one of the patients. Staring at me with a blank expression on his face, he suddenly grabbed my shoulders and started to shake me, shouting, "Bitch, Bitch." I somehow managed to free myself. I was so shocked and unable to think straight. What could I do? I must protect the patients. Mr Leach was clearly very confused and aggressive. Patients were waking, unaware what was happening. It was pandemonium. In a state of sheer panic, I managed to reach the ward door, opening it and shouting for help. Staff from the ward opposite heard my cries and within minutes help arrived. Mr Leach was soon restrained while I administered a sedative injection. He continued to call me names until he fell asleep.

Patient behaviour can be so unpredictable during the night. The ward was in turmoil when my nurse returned. Some of the patients were very upset by the incident, but Mr Leach was fully recovered after a sleep and never called me names again.

## Chapter 32

Spring has arrived and it almost feels like summer. The temperature has risen considerably over the past few weeks. It feels good to get the cold, miserable winter behind us, but for me it is not of much consequence. I seem to be working all the time. I am exhausted, unable to enjoy any leisure time I have. I had forgotten how tiring night duty was. My seven nights off are spent trying to recover from my nine nights at work. My relationship with Andrew feels to be struggling; we rarely get the chance to see each other. I have decided to return to day duty after spending some time on the coronary care unit.

Nursing practice was continually changing as a result of medical advances, and coronary units along with intensive care units grew rapidly. The coronary unit consisted of eight beds full of patients suffering from severe heart conditions. Resuscitation was becoming central to clinical practice. No hospital could afford to be without the latest techniques and equipment. 'Crash' was a term familiar to all staff, indicating that a patient had suffered a cardiac arrest. Doctors, nurses and technicians were taught the techniques and needed to practise. It was an exciting time to be working in medicine. New drugs were being introduced and resuscitation was frequently performed. We could bring patients back to life! Being a qualified nurse, I had dealt with many cardiac arrests but it hadn't prepared me for working on the unit. It was a different world. Doctor Adrian Freeman was my saviour. He was a senior houseman, very friendly and approachable. My anxiety melted away as he breezed into the unit, introducing himself with a strong hand shake.

"Hi, Staff Nurse Clark," he said, glancing at my name badge. "I don't think we have met before. I'm on call tonight and will be trying to get some shut-eye in the room outside the unit. Any concerns just come and wake me."

"Oh thanks. I'm feeling rather nervous as I've never worked on the unit before. I'm unfamiliar with a lot of the equipment and not proficient at reading electrocardiograms. I feel clueless looking at the heart tracings on the screens," I said.

"I will bring you some information on ECGs. You might get a chance to look at it. Don't worry; I'm at hand if you need me."

With the help of Adrian I soon became competent in the running of the unit. I gained expertise in dealing with cardiac arrest, but resuscitation drained me, both mentally and physically. It could be such a violent procedure. Many lives were thankfully saved and some patients were able to live a fulfilling life, but not all resuscitation was successful. In some cases would it not have been a wiser decision to allow the patient to have a natural death? Nearing the end of my night duty I was feeling disillusioned. It was so depressing at times. Why was there so much sadness? Why did some patients have to suffer so much? It all seemed so unfair. It was all getting too much for me to cope with. I jump at the sound of the telephone ringing.

"Coronary care unit. Staff Nurse Clark speaking."

"Found you at last. This is Nurse Dawson on male surgical. We have a patient on the ward asking if you are still working at the hospital. You nursed him on ward 1 at the Old Infirmary following a severe road traffic accident."

It was Michael – four years later, and he still remembered me. He was still having surgery following his accident.

"Oh how wonderful. I'd love to see him. Is it okay if I pop down sometime during the night to see him?" I asked.

"Yes fine. He is recovering well and should be discharged soon. I won't tell him I have spoken to you, can't wait to see his reaction," she said excitedly.

It was early hours in the morning when I managed to visit the surgical ward. Michael was fast asleep. He had changed beyond all recognition. I looked at him in wonderment; there in front of me was a fine, healthy looking young man with no resemblance to the frail Michael I had nursed on ward 1. Was it really the same person? The tears were beginning to well up as I gently woke him.

"Hi Michael, thought I'd just pop in to see you."

He looked at me blankly. Silence.

"Bet you don't recognise me?" I said, smiling at him.

His eyes lit up. "I can't believe it. Is it really Nurse Clark, or should I say Staff Nurse Clark? It's wonderful to see you after such a long time. I didn't think you would still be at the hospital. Can I give you a hug to make sure I'm not dreaming?"

We soon engaged in conversation, like long lost friends. I hadn't realised Nurse Clark, the novice, had made such an impression on him. Seeing Michael looking so well convinced me I was making a difference to people's lives.

Yet again he had restored my faith in the job I was doing. Michael was discharged several days later. I never saw him again.

# Chapter 33

The mid-summer heat was helping to lift my spirits. I was relieved to be back on day duty, working on my favourite medical ward. Some of the characters, like Mr Tully and Jim, had been discharged, replaced by other patients who were able to liven the ward up. The depression I had felt while working on the coronary care unit had lifted. Sad days were often offset by the happy times on the ward.

It was a busy Saturday morning. I was expecting Mr Harris to do a ward round and he was already an hour late.

"When is the boss arriving?" questioned Mr Reed angrily. "I was hoping to be going home today."

Mr Reed was a miserable character. He was in his late thirties, had a high powered job and was full of his own importance, talking incessantly, continually demanding attention and complaining. He had been on the ward a few days suffering from angina, but thankfully it had settled with medication. I would be glad to see the back of him.

"I've no idea Mr Reed. I expected him a while ago," I replied.

"Can't you contact him to find out how long he will be?" he asked, his face turning a bright shade of red.

"Sorry. That's not possible. He should be here shortly."

I was hoping to get the ward round out of the way; it was something I dreaded. Mr Harris didn't improve, he was consistently in a foul mood! Late afternoon and Mr

Harris still hadn't arrived. More patients were beginning to complain which was unsettling Mr Reed further.

"This is not acceptable. I suggest we should all complain," he said.

"I'm sorry folks. I'm not happy either but I can't do anything about it. I'm going out with my boyfriend tonight and don't want to be late off duty. I have no idea where Mr Harris is."

I was puzzled as Mr Reed went quiet, focusing on something behind me. "Mr Harris happens to be here," said a grumpy voice. I turned slowly to be confronted by a none too pleased Mr Harris. How embarrassing! The ward round was more unpleasant than usual.

I was late yet again leaving the ward. Such a shame we didn't get paid for overtime. I was soon dolled up, eagerly running to catch the bus. Andrew and I were seeing less and less of each other. We were so much in love but for some reason our relationship appeared to be struggling.

We had a wonderful time – a romantic meal followed by a night at Lord Jim's disco. I returned to the hospital early in the morning with a pounding head and blistered feet. I should manage a few hours' sleep before my early shift. But the fire escape door was locked! I had forgotten to arrange for it to be left open. A twenty-two-year-old shouldn't be in this position.

What could I do? I mustn't get caught. All the rooms were in darkness. In desperation I started to throw pebbles at the windows but was unable to rouse anyone. Near to tears I hobbled to the local park. It would soon be getting light and there would be a bench for me to sit on. I needed to rest my aching feet.

A beautiful summer dawn was breaking as I observed a tramp lying on the next bench covered by a newspaper. He was filthy. Rubbish was strewn around him. It saddened me to see such a pitiful sight. He looked so alone. Why was he living like this? Didn't anyone care about him? How had he got into this state? It reminded me of Bill and the revulsion I had felt on first meeting him. I smiled at the thought of how proud he had been when I manicured his nails. He was such a lovely man. This tramp soon started to stir, groaning and stretching. It was time to return to the hospital.

My relationship with Andrew finished soon afterwards. It was an amicable split but I was distraught, sitting on my bedroom floor unable to stop crying. My heart was breaking. I destroyed all his letters and photographs in the hope it would ease the pain, something that I later regretted. I was inconsolable. It was time for me to move on.

I saw Andrew once more before leaving Huddersfield, when he unexpectedly returned my umbrella which I had left at his parents' house. We talked for ages. It felt so sad. We were right for each other but had met at the wrong time. I was ambitious, wanting to further my nursing career and not yet ready to settle down.

I met Andrew again over thirty years later at his mother's funeral. He was there with his wife and three grown-up children. It felt surreal talking to him again. Surprisingly we had both married on the same day but our lives had been very different. I was pleased that he had found such happiness.

# Chapter 34

Time flies by as I pack my suitcases. How had I managed to accumulate so much stuff? With mixed emotions I keep dissolving into tears. It had been my home for over four years. Was it really my last day in Huddersfield? I looked back with fond memories. It seemed a lifetime ago that I arrived, a naive teenager struggling to get used to the strict discipline and long working hours. The friendliness and warmth of many of my colleagues, and the help and support we gave each other. The late night study sessions we spent together, the humour we shared, but most of all the laughter. We were like a family. Sadly it would be impossible to keep in touch with them all.

Times were changing as some of the nurses I had trained with had already left. Linda had decided nursing was not the career for her. Most of the Irish girls had returned to Ireland to continue their nursing careers. Mary and Bridget were staying at the hospital for a while to gain more experience before deciding which pathway to take. I would soon be starting my midwifery training in Coventry with Ann. Dad was picking me up in the evening, to help with my luggage. How would I have coped without his taxi service? Having time to spare I decided to have a last stroll around the hospital grounds. I had said my goodbye to everyone and now needed to be alone. What a glorious day: bright sunshine, the familiar scent of freshly cut grass filling the air. A group of young nurses walk past me laughing uncontrollably. How I envied them. I am overcome with nostalgia as I start to daydream. I will miss the good times. The work has been exhausting but I have thoroughly enjoyed nursing. Helping patients to feel better has given me great satisfaction.

Maybe nursing was a calling after all. Some of the patients I will never forget: Michael, Edith, Mr Tully, Mr James, Bill and Jim in particular. They all meant so much to me. I smile at the thought of some of the antics on the medical ward and the humour of many of the patients: Jim's nightly streaking, Mr Tully and the cornflakes, and my successful role play as Denise when attending to Edith and her budgie. In contrast, the sorrow I felt when Mr James died will never leave me.

I remember all the fun we had and the mischief we got up to, breaking the rules of the nurses' home, staying out all night, drinking too much, climbing up the fire escape in the early hours of the morning. It helped us to cope with such a physical and emotional job. How I will miss the camaraderie. I begin to wish that I was staying. Had I made the wrong decision?

Dad arrives, and fills the boot of the car with my suitcases. Holding back the tears, I glance back at the hospital as we leave.

# Chapter 35

It was a mid-summer's day in the late 1990s when I next visited the hospital as an out-patient. It felt surreal being a patient at the hospital where I had worked all those years ago. Memories came flooding back. I remembered those years in the late 1960s with great fondness. It was such a fascinating time. The cataclysm of the war was over and we were experiencing an explosion of freedom, which enabled us to enjoy the little free time we had from the long hours we were expected to work.

The main entrance appeared somewhat smaller and darker than I remembered and was looking quite dated. A pleasant lady welcomed me at the reception desk and pointed me in the direction of the out-patients' department. I was in no doubt when I had arrived. Everywhere was very busy and noisy with long queues of patients anxiously waiting to be seen.

The usual rumbles of dissatisfaction could be heard as people complained about the long wait, the staff rushing around doing their best. It was a familiar scene: some things never change. Accepting that I was in for a long wait I decided to have a stroll around the hospital where my thoughts reflected back to what life was like in my nursing days. I remembered the hospital when it ran itself as a virtually independent, self-functioning organism where the nurses nursed, the cleaners cleaned and the doctors did their rounds. Everyone did their jobs as well and as professionally as they knew how. Management consisted of a small number of people, Matron being in charge of standards in nursing care. As I remember everything seemed to run smoothly. The NHS staff were prepared to put up with long working hours for no great amount of pay. Matron had now been replaced by several smartly dressed managers. The senior nurses' offices along the main corridor now appeared to house managers and administrators who I could imagine would be busy negotiating and drawing up contracts and ensuring their implementation. Sadly the vision of Matron was long gone, replaced by administrators who needn't necessarily have had nursing or hospital experience. I wondered if the hospital ran as efficiently.

I became emotional walking around the hospital grounds. The nurses' home and school of nursing had long gone, although the building still stood. I was unsure what it was now used for. Hesitating as I passed the building, I could almost hear the laughter of my friends. I remembered Barbara as I imagined the grassed area we frequently tip-toed across early in the morning after a night at the disco. Poor Sister Brooks must have had a difficult job trying to discipline young nurses. Nursing has seen so many changes since then. When nursing became a university course in the mid-eighties, out went some of the dedication, compassion, self-control and respect. In their place came a new kind of nurse. Instead of being taught as before by doctors and nurse tutors, aspiring nurses did student-centred courses in sociology, psychology, micro-biology, and management. They were assessed for their communication, management and problem solving skills. Specific clinical skills seemed to be rarely mentioned. Did our training in the 1960s equip us better to nurse? Many nurses had become unhappy at the changes in the 1990s and were leaving the profession. I had now qualified as a Midwife and Health visitor and was fortunate to be working in the community where the level of unrest was much less.

I returned to out-patients feeling refreshed following my trip down memory lane. Was I looking back through rose-tinted glasses? Were things really much better in my day or had I forgotten the unpleasant parts? The queues were now much shorter, the atmosphere was more relaxed, and the patients seemed a lot happier. The nurse's uniforms had no resemblance to the ones we wore. They were more practical and comfortable to wear, made of soft fabric in a relaxed style. Gone were the caps, the wide starched belts and collars which caused such discomfort and chafing of the neck. Make-up was now permitted.

My name was soon called. The long wait had allowed me to reflect on a time long forgotten.

Today changes are continually being made in the nursing profession. Student nurses now have more practical placements than in the 1990s, enabling them to spend more time at the bedside learning clinical skills and how to efficiently care for ill patients. The work has changed since my day but it remains hard mentally, physically and emotionally. Following recent hospital experiences, I found the nurses today remain equally as dedicated and caring. What changes will we see in the nursing profession over the next fifty years? I wondered on my way home.